BECOMING THE BEST

This book would not be complete without mentioning David Kynaston – a real-life mentor and enthusiast on Total Quality

BECOMING THE BEST

HOW TO GAIN COMPANY-WIDE COMMITMENT TO TOTAL QUALITY

Barry Popplewell
and
Alan Wildsmith

SQI
Strategic Quality Initiatives

Gower

Published by
Gower Publishing Company Limited
Gower House
Croft Road
Aldershot
Hants GU11 3HR
England

ISBN 0 566 02798 4

The characters and situations in this book are entirely imaginary and bear
no relation to any real person or actual happening.

Printed and bound in Great Britain by
Anchor Brendon Ltd, Tiptree, Essex

Contents

Neil	Chief Executive
Tony	Sales
Peter	Production
Roger	Finance
Fred	Commercial
Simone	Personnel
Derek	Technical
Harold	Quality

1 "The day had started bad. It couldn't get any worse."

Business had been good that year, almost too good to be true. A buoyant market, lots of orders without too much sales effort, some with real wallet busting potential. Exchange rates had been favourable when it really mattered, labour relations quiet, relatively speaking. No health and safety panics, no emergencies or major problems, no disasters anyway. Morale hadn't been too bad either, in fact the whole outfit had been buzzing all year. No doubt about it, the opportunity had been there, a chance to change the fortunes of the organization, an open window in fact. And he'd blown it.

Neil Johnson lifted his eyes from Roger's financial report and considered his options. The promised improvement in results hadn't happened after all. Promises, promises, he thought, gloomily, sitting back in his chair. The warning bells had been ringing long enough.

Neil took several deep breaths, drawing on his inner resources. He wasn't the man to let bad news get the better of him. He prided himself on his resilience. He was a positive thinker, a man of action. He had this rare talent, this ability to shut out bad news, close his eyes to failure and turn instead to something positive. He was a man of character, with a strong sense of responsibility. He was the Director, the Boss. He piloted the ship, held the helm, made the decisions.

With a sigh reaching the depths of his bowels Neil shouldered his responsibilities. He took his pen and memo-pad, addressed the top line to his co-directors and against subject wrote 'Year End Report'. In the blank space under the subject heading he scribbled 'Comment?' He gazed thought-fully at his work. The scribble imparted a sense of urgency to the word but was it strong enough? Neil was a good judge of character, he knew his peers, they would simply initial the damned report and send it back. He crossed out 'Comment?' and wrote 'Why?' He was a man of few words, they would know what he meant. When he asked a question he expected an answer; they knew that too. On the other hand they could quite legitimately respond, 'Why what?' and send it back for clarification.

He had to be more precise. Irritation began to gnaw at his stomach as he scribbled through 'Why?' and wrote 'What went wrong?' underneath the scribble. He put down his pen and began to drum on the desk, reviewing the situation. He could feel his irritation change to anger as his mind dwelt on the responses he already knew he would get from his fellow directors, his team. He stopped drumming on the desk, ripped the top sheet off the memo pad and crushed it into a tight little ball before flinging it into the bin. On the new top sheet he wrote afresh in large block letters BOARD MEETING 10 AM! Underneath that he added TODAY!!

The board room was airy and light, simply and comfortably furnished with table and chairs and four soft leather seats which reclined in a corner adjacent to a large picture window. Ultra modern and original works of art were mounted on each of two opposing walls and there were two doors, one opening out from Neil's office, the other giving access from the corridor. Outside, a well manicured lawn had been planted with seven tall cypress trees while in the near distance an evergreen shrubbery softened the lower outline of five massive boulders. The whole setting, both inside and out, was designed to give the inhabitants a feeling of maximum security. No matter how bad the reality of the day, in here it could never be as bad as it really was.

Neil opened his door at 10 o'clock precisely. A quick survey as he strode across the room confirmed that his co-directors were all present; Tony, sales; Peter, manufacturing; Roger, financial administration; Fred, commercial, and Derek, technical. They were all there. He put the financial report on the table, squarely in front of his own chair, and sat down.

"Thank you for coming at such short notice," he began politely, controlling his emotional state. "This is an extra-ordinary meeting. I've called it because we're in trouble."

Tony knew they were in trouble, deep trouble. But how did Neil know about it? He stared at him. "How d'you know?" he asked. "Who told you?"

Neil stared back at him, frowning. He tapped the report in front of him. "Roger told me."

"Who told Roger?" Tony asked, shifting his query across the table to the administration director. "Who told you, Roger?"

Neil's careful preparations were falling apart, rapidly. He took command, irritation rising in his voice. "His accountants. His system, the whole computerized system told him. We're here to discuss Roger's year-end financial report. What are you on about, Tony?"

Tony weighed up the pros and cons. Neil obviously didn't know what he knew – that was good. It meant he could choose his own time to break the news. Roger's report was annoying Neil and could reasonably be expected to divert his attention away from his own news. That, too, was good. Neil would be kept busy enough biting lumps out of everybody for not controlling their budgets and that meant he would be unable to concentrate on him, Tony, alone. That was good; he might emerge from this relatively unscathed. On the other hand . . .

"Tony! Could we have your attention, please?"

Neil's unnerving habit of speaking through clenched teeth imparted an abnormal ferocity to his voice. He only did it when he was angry.

"Sorry, Neil," said Tony, "It's not been a very good day up to now" he added, apologetically.

"It's going to get worse," Neil promised. Picking up the financial report, he waved it in the air like a flag before throwing it on to the middle of the table.

"I won't bore you with the details," he said. "Just the bottom line. As a balance sheet our trading results are balanced. By a curious quirk of statistics, we have managed to make an absolute zero. No profit, no loss." He paused and looked directly at each of his peers in turn, allowing time for the bottom line to sink in. Satisfied that it had sunk in Neil continued to emphasize the situation. "No profit, no loss," he repeated, "in a year when our trading conditions could hardly have been better. And this, a no profit result, after three years of slogging our way through an almighty renewal programme. Look at it."

Neil unclenched his fist and ticked off each point like a hammer striking a xylophone.

"The very latest cash flow monitoring system, stock reduction, stores, work in progress, computerized accounts, computerized order processing, vast amounts spent on modernizing plant, headcount reduction, twenty per cent leaner than two years ago. We've spent money to make money. But where is it? Where is the profit? What is going wrong?"

Again Neil surveyed his compatriots, looking directly into each pair of eyes in turn. His first salvo was fired.

Roger stared out through the big picture window. A silver glow outlined the clouds which were building up in the

West. His eyes focused on the huge boulders in the rock garden. He knew how much they had cost to transport.

Derek, the technical director, broke the silence which followed Neil's question.

"If we're going wrong," he said, laying emphasis on his first word. "If we're going wrong, the answer must be contained somewhere in Roger's report."

Roger brought his attention back into the board room.

"All the improvements we've made, Neil, they all cost money, big money. Computers aren't cheap, software systems aren't cheap."

"We're not in business to keep the computer companies in business, Roger. We're in business to make a profit. Where is the return on investment? There isn't even a smell of it in Roger's report, and if there's no return, there's no improvement. Is there?"

Roger flushed easily.

"Don't blame me. I didn't ask for all the damn things. I didn't do all the justifications."

Neil ignored him and turned to face Derek.

"What do you mean by if, Derek? If we're going wrong? You know as well as I do where the money came from for our renewal programme. You know the promises we made, correction, the promises I made. You know where the investment has gone. Into the technical and commercial sectors. No, let's personalize it. You, Peter and Fred, have between you spent ninety per cent of the money. And what do you have to show for it? Nothing. So I ask again, what do you mean by if we're going wrong?"

"I mean we would have been out of business by now if we hadn't made those investments. And I still say that the answer must be contained somewhere in Roger's report."

"No, Derek. The answer is not in Roger's report. Think again."

Derek didn't look at Neil. Instead he addressed the work of art on the wall opposite.

"Our products are well designed. They're well made. We have a reasonable market share."

While Derek continued to inform the work of art how reasonable their situation really was, Peter was only half listening. His other half was doodling with the reality of their situation. Morale, he wrote, then a dash, lousy. Profit – worse. Competition – Japs, Yanks, Koreans, Mongolians!

Tony also was doodling. On his scrap pad he was making patterns with the initials BNT. As each pattern was complete he crossed it out such that the initials were obliterated. Tony was feeling utterly miserable. Torn two ways, undecided as to how and when he should break the news. The decent thing, he knew, was to see Neil on his own and ease him in gently. Give him time to consider the problem. Neil would eat him alive. The alternative was to speak up now while Neil was still distracted by Roger's report.

Tony sighed heavily. He hated indecision. Especially in himself. He half heard Derek mention the word customers and how reasonably well satisfied they were. Reluctantly he decided there was safety in numbers. He held up his hand to stop Derek in mid-stream. Neil beat him to it.

"Cut it Derek," he said, feigning weariness. "What does well designed mean? What does well made mean? What's all this reasonable business?" He paused, neither expecting nor wanting a reply. "Your job," he went on, "Your job as technical director is not to make sure we have well designed products. Peter isn't here to make sure your designs are well made. Tony's job isn't to ensure we have a reasonable share of the market." He faced them all. "If that's what you all think your jobs are, then I'm beginning to think I know where the answer is. And it isn't in Roger's report!"

Tony's hand was still up in the air, hovering between supporting his chin and a half-hearted wave. He caught Neil's eye and then wished he hadn't.

"Yes, Tony? You going to give me the answer?"

Tony cleared his throat. "BNT" he said, louder than he would have liked. Tony stopped, realizing too late that he had made the fatal mistake of introducing a subject without adequate preparation. Normally his wits would have saved him but at this moment they deserted him utterly. His brain was empty, void.

"Yes?" prompted Neil, "What's BNT got to do with it?"

BNT was a huge organization, rich as Croeseus, Swiss based and by far and above their biggest account. Twenty per cent of their sales volume was delivered to BNT on a weekly call-off to seven destinations throughout Western Europe. BNT alone accounted for nearly one quarter of their annual turnover. It also accounted for periodic expense account trips to Geneva, Berne, Paris, Luxembourg, Brussels, Hamburg and Berlin. BNT was a good customer. The best. Neil sensed approaching doom. It was written on Tony's face. Gently, rolling both hands, like a ground traffic controller guiding a jumbo on to the grid, he coaxed Tony into speech.

"Come on Tony. It's all right. Let's have it. What about BNT?"

"They're not very happy with us."

"Not very happy?"

"We've dropped a few too many clangers recently."

"Go on."

"They're very unhappy with us."

Neil stared. "We've lost them?"

Tony nodded. "Gomez telexed me. He's closed the account."

There was silence in the board room. The day had started bad. It couldn't get any worse. But it had got worse. This was the big one.

Neil bowed his head, overcome by a feeling of peace and serenity, a great spiritual calm. Maybe death is like this, he thought. The end of the road.

He was knocked sideways for several moments, seconds or minutes, he didn't know. Time had no meaning. When he recovered he lifted his head, almost happy. The issues were clear. He knew what he had to do.

"Gomez isn't the boss."

"He is as far as we're concerned. You know Gomez, he's director of purchasing for the whole of BNT."

"Yes of course I know Gomez and he isn't the boss. Piet van Oust is the boss. I've got a lot of respect for Piet. Very capable. Very human. I'll talk to him."

Tony's misery was not relieved. He knew the score. Business practice did not include the humanities.

"Have you got the telex with you?"

Tony passed it to Peter to pass to Neil. Peter already knew the contents.

The telex was a thick wad of several folded sheets. Neil held it by the top of the first sheet and allowed it to open in free fall. It was over a metre long.

"How many accounts have we got with BNT?" he asked.

"Only one. It's handled centrally through Geneva."

Tony had regained his composure. He was on safe ground. He knew BNT's organization like the back of his hand.

"All the staff functions are managed from head office," he explained, "from Geneva. Their data is computerized.

Neil scanned the first sheets of the telex as he talked.

"So is ours," he said.

Peter spoke up. "No," he said, "not really. Ours

only covers the technical and commercial sectors. Theirs covers all their activities, including purchasing and quality."

He almost added, that's how they've got us, but held his tongue in time. Tony should have discussed the telex with Neil first but it had been too explosive. In brief, single-line statements it listed every problem BNT had experienced from them over the past six months. Tony had gone straight to Peter with it.

Neil's frown deepened as he read on.

"This is awful," he said, "it must be wrong. We can't possibly be as bad as this. Charging them for things we haven't shipped, not charging them for things we have shipped. Goods ordered for Luxembourg ending up in Berlin, goods held pending receipt of release notes." He looked up. "Did you know about these problems, Fred?" he asked.

Fred was an older man, close to retirement, director of the commercial division. He adjusted his glasses before replying.

"Well, I know we have had some complaints from Berne, some from Paris. I think we've had a few from Luxembourg as well. Nothing much. We put them right as soon as we know what the problem is."

Neil looked at him, incredulously.

"Nothing much?" he asked, waving the lengthy telex like a banner. "Nothing much? Is that what you'd be thinking if we had to send a telex like this to one of our suppliers? And what about your new computerized system? Isn't that supposed to stop this sort of thing?"

"We're still on the learning curve, Neil," Fred replied, patiently. "We've got to expect a few teething problems."

"Computers haven't got teeth," said Neil, baring his own. "They can only think one way, the right way. They can only make one decision, the right decision. So how come ours are shipping goods to Berlin that ought to have gone to Luxembourg?"

Fred gave Tony a withering look.

"We arrange shipment of whatever to wherever as directed by the Sales desks. It isn't my fault if they get it wrong."

Neil referred back to the telex, saying, "Not your fault. I see. What about billing Geneva for goods they haven't ordered and we haven't shipped?" Before Fred could reply Neil scrubbed the question. "Oh, no," he groaned, "you couldn't. But you did. Look at this. How could you possibly have put a hold on urgently required shipments to Paris, and then add insult to injury by demanding payment before delivery? And look, it's incredible, the reason you gave is that BNT is entered on our books as a bad commercial risk due to non-payment of previous invoices."

Neil let the telex fall onto the table from which it slid onto the floor. He shook his head.

"Somebody's out to ruin us," he said grimly. "It's sabotage, commercial sabotage. BNT, rich as Creoseus, a bad commercial risk. Oh yes. That entry must have been a deliberate ploy by somebody working for the competition. They're trying to steal BNT away from us. Find him, Fred."

Fred glowered at Roger. "It's not sabotage, Neil," he said, patience beginning to wear thin. "It's happened before. Not to BNT, I hasten to add, but it has happened a few times before. When the Sales desks get it wrong," he explained, "and we invoice a customer for goods he didn't order and we did or didn't ship, the customer gets thirty days in which to pay up. If, instead of paying up he ships back to us the goods he didn't order then we can raise a credit note which cancels the invoice. If he doesn't do this within ninety days he goes into admin's bad debtors' book and a 'hold further shipments' instruction is punched into the computer's data bank against his code number. Now, if he can't ship back the goods he didn't order because we misdirected the shipment to wherever the Sales desk told us to and the customer therefore has no goods to return, all he has to do is to inform us, either by returning the invoice or by letter or even a telephone call. We check into it, and if he's right and we got it wrong, again we cancel the invoice. But if he doesn't bother to tell us, for whatever reason, maybe because somebody's poorly or because he knows he didn't receive the goods and didn't order them anyway, so he just puts the invoice in the bin, well . . ." Fred glowered again at Roger, "ninety days later he's in Roger's bad debtor's book."

Roger gave Fred a real prissy stare. "And occasionally," retorted Roger, determined that this should not be all one-sided, "Occasionally, when Fred's girls put the wrong address on the invoice, the customer doesn't get an invoice for goods he didn't order and didn't receive. And ninety days later, we have no option but to enter him into the bad debtors book."

Neil was listening to all this in utter disbelief. He followed the logic of the explanation almost in a state of shock.

"Tell me, somebody," he said. "How does a customer get out of the bad debtors' book?"

"By paying his outstanding debts," Roger said.

"For goods he didn't order, hasn't received and isn't invoiced? How can he pay what he doesn't owe and doesn't know about? He's completely innocent."

Roger shuffled uncomfortably in his chair. "It gets sorted out eventually, Neil."

"When eventually?"

It was Fred's turn to be uncomfortable.

"When he complains about an overdue shipment of goods he really has ordered and hasn't received," he said.

"Like BNT Paris?"

Fred nodded. "Like BNT Paris," he agreed.

Neil turned the knife. Not to cause pain, that was a side effect, an added bonus. His main aim was a dogged determination to understand this whole lunatic process. Intellectual curiosity was driving him.

"But we all know about BNT," he said, softly. "They pay on time. We even have special prices for BNT because they don't delay payment. They're our best customer. Nearly one quarter of our annual turnover is with BNT. We all know that. Who could possibly even consider entering BNT into a bad debtors' book?"

Roger took a few seconds before replying. "Staff replacements," he said. "New employees. It's easy for them to make mistakes. They're eager, keen to get on with the job, don't know enough to know when to ask questions. It's easy, Neil."

Fred nodded a sober agreement. He was firmly on Roger's side.

Neil said nothing, didn't even register that he had heard the explanation.

"I called this board meeting" he said, leaning over to pick up the telex, "with the intention of finding out why we are not making a profit. Roger's report is factual but historical fact. The answer to the question is not contained in Roger's report." He looked pointedly at Derek, who said nothing.

"This is where the answer is," he went on, waving the lengthy telex again. "It's an expensive way to get an answer, maybe it will prove too expensive. We'll know that after I've talked to Piet van Oust. But this is where the profit is going. People failures, system failures, organization failures. If this is what we're doing to BNT we must be doing it to all our customers. And that's what is eating up our profits. Errors, faults, corrections, over and over again. We must be riddled with it."

"Peter," he said. "Pop out and ask Sylvia to bring in

some coffee, will you. Tea for those who prefer it. We're going to go through this telex line by line. I'll need to know how to play it when I talk to Geneva. A lot of it I can blame on the new computer system, but some of them . . . " he shook his head. "How am I going to explain away a half eaten pork pie in one of the shipments to Berne?" Peter was at the door on his way out. He turned round.

"There is an explanation, Neil," he said. "I've sacked him."

Outside, Peter stopped to light a cigarette before going to look for Sylvia. It was going to be a long session. He'd seen the telex earlier than Neil and knew most of the answers. Some of them Neil wasn't going to like.

2 "Facts . . . the bright stepping stones of logic."

It was ten past three and the board room was empty. Except for Neil. Neil was down, demoralized, depressed.

The problems raised by BNT had caused arguments and accusations touching every department. Nobody was clean, nobody. Neil stayed down. He couldn't get up, overshadowed as he was by the immensity of the problem.

After ten minutes of trying to sort out his thoughts, three million brain cells finally linked up in a particular pattern and gave him a new thought to examine. Neil locked on to it and immediately felt happier. He knew what was wrong. Now that he knew what was wrong he could do something about it. This was a better situation than the one he had been in first thing this morning when he had read Roger's report. In fact it was a much better situation. He not only knew why there was no profit but he also knew, from listening to the accusations and counter accusations, that his divisional directors between them knew what was causing the errors and corrections that were eating up all the profits.

The solution was obvious. All they had to do was talk together and find ways around the problems they were causing each other. Then they should get their department heads to talk together in the same way, and after that the department heads should get all their people. . . . Neil's progression of logic came to a full stop. He couldn't have everybody in the organization talking to everybody else in the organization. Nobody would ever get any work done. And anyway, it wasn't a static situation. If Neil had learned anything at all in his years at work there was one thing he knew for sure. No living organization remained static; it was ever changing, growing or dying; there was no in-between.

He went back to the beginning and re-examined the hopeful thought he had had. It was impractical if not impossible for the whole work force to talk to each other but at least his directors could start the ball rolling. It was so easy, so obvious. Nothing was that easy. If it was this whole situation would never have arisen.

Neil groaned out loud. He wasn't getting anywhere. His thoughts were going around in circles, skirting round the problem. Logic was needed, logic and simplicity. Desperation drove him back to a review of the facts in all their stark simplicity. Immediately he felt a sense of relief. Facts were facts, pure and simple. They shone like stars in a black sky. There was no confusion in a fact, no tangled web of ifs and buts, no emotion, no deceit and best of all, facts were not subject to the universal law of graduation; they either were or were not, there was no in-between stage. Facts were the bright clean stepping stones of logic. Manfully, Neil set about reviewing the facts, setting them firmly in the quagmire of his situation.

Fact one, the organization had made huge invest-ments in the most up-to-date plant and techniques. Fact two, zero profit. Logical deduction, the investments had not resulted in operating profits. Any other deduction could only be pure conjecture. Fact three, the BNT telex listed faults, errors and problems witnessed by seven BNT sites over a six-month period. Fact four, there was nothing difficult or peculiar about BNT as a customer. The logical deduction was that all his customers were experiencing a similar pattern of failures. He had lost BNT but not his other customers. Maybe the reason for this was that their expectations were lower than BNT's. Or maybe he was losing customers left right and centre without knowing it. He made a mental note to query this with Tony. Fact five, he continued thoughtfully, discussion of the items listed in the BNT telex had revealed a horrendous picture of errors and rework caused by the left hand not knowing, and even worse, not caring, what the right hand was doing. Logical deduction, this was the nub of the problem, this was what was eating up the profits. This was the problem he had to solve.

It was 3.30 when Neil left the board room. Armed with the BNT telex he went straight through his own office into the outer room, his secretary's office. "Sylvia," he said. "Phone Harold. Tell him I'm coming down to see him."

Harold was his quality assurance manager. It seemed like a fairly logical first step.

The route took him through the sales department. Fresh-faced youths, confident, competent looking men, women in spring dresses, modern desks, data terminals. Everything looked clean and healthy, efficient. As he strode through Neil wondered how many of them, even now, were making mistakes that would have to be corrected somewhere else, eating up his profit, losing him the very customers they were employed to keep. Some nodded and smiled to him as he passed through. It was not in him to be two-faced. He was angry with them; they had let him down, lost BNT. Neil kept his face like flint leaving an icy wake behind him.

Into the commercial department. There they were, clean looking men and women, data terminals, keyboards, VDUs, the very latest, the most up-to-date high technology equipment. Even now, these self-same clean looking people were sending out instructions which would result in goods going to Lagos instead of London, incomplete shipments, wrong quantities, more irate customers, more money down the drain.

Neil carried on. It was all of a hundred metres to the quality assurance department and each step was firing his temper. He knew he wasn't being fair. He should have asked Harold to come up to his office. Instead he had acted impulsively, hadn't prepared for the meeting, hadn't thought it through.

He stopped by the vending machine, deliberately calming down, soothing his temper. All he wanted from Harold was the facts; he wasn't going to bite him.

Calmer, he fished around in his trouser pockets, found a coin and pushed it through the slot. The vending machine chunked and gave him a penny change. He pressed two buttons for coffee, white, no sugar, and waited. The machine hummed dutifully and began to pour whitish coffee from the top of its recess into the drain at the bottom of the recess. Hastily Neil hit the face of the vending machine with the heel of his hand. He hit it again, harder and again until a plastic cup dropped into the recess, just as the flow of coffee stopped. Neil restrained himself. He searched his pockets and found nothing. Feeling strangely foolish, he took his penny change out of the machine and continued along the corridor to Harold's office.

Harold had had rather a good day. During the morning's technical meeting he had successfully argued the case for delaying the release of a new product into the market until three potential safety hazards had been put right. Over lunch he had entertained a visiting customer's inspection engineer who had checked out a major order to the value of tens of thousands. The problems he had found were only minor ones, easily dealt with. In fact he had dealt with them straight after lunch so that Mr Johnson could see they were on the ball. He had caught up with his mail after Mr Johnson had left. His in-tray was empty, desk clean, out-tray reasonably full. Harold was on top of the job, confident, expansive. Even an unexpected visit from the boss gave him no cause for nervousness. Sylvia hadn't enlightened him. "How's quality these days Harold?" asked Neil innocently by way of introduction while at the same time pulling a chair out from under the table which was endways on to Harold's desk. He sat down and put the BNT telex on the table in front of him.

Harold had been with the organization for eighteen years. He knew it inside out, another reason for confidence in the job. He had seen four managing directors come and go and had worked for Neil since his appointment three years ago. He liked Neil, thought he was the best managing director the organization had ever had.

Neil's introductory question put Harold immediately on guard. He knew Neil. The question was not a hypothetical one, thrown out by way of introduction. Neil's face belied the even tone of his voice. Something was wrong. He could sense it. Maybe it was something to do with that telex.

His thought process moved like lightning. During split seconds of consideration and evaluation he opted finally for the relaxed, semi-humorous approach.

"Not an easy question to answer, Neil," he said. "It's heads you win, tails I lose. If I say quality isn't a problem you'll think I've got an easy job. If I say quality is a problem you'll think I'm not doing my job properly."

"Harold!" growled Neil, warningly, his voice beginning to match the expression on his face. "I don't want a debate. I want to know what you think of the quality put out by this organization. Is it good or bad?"

Harold eased himself up and out of his chair. He had misjudged the situation. The boss was angrier than he had thought. He moved across to the table and pulled out a chair next to Neil. He sat down. He couldn't be glared at here, and he could also scan the telex, get some idea of what this was all about.

"Technically," said Harold, choosing his words carefully. "Technically our quality is good. We have a first class quality system that makes sure it stays good. We have the highest national and international approvals and we're under constant surveillance by external quality assurance assessors to make sure that we maintain our standards. Our quality costs are reasonable." He sensed rather than heard a growl beginning to emerge from his boss's throat.

"I mean," he went on hurriedly, trying to pre-empt the comment. "Our quality costs are normal for our activities."

"Reasonable? Normal?" said Neil having difficulty keeping his voice down. "How can they be reasonable? What's normal?"

He leaned forward and round to look Harold straight in the eyes. "Do you know how much profit we've made? Nothing. That's how much, not a penny piece. Is that normal? Is that reasonable?"

Harold did some quick thinking. Neil must have got the year end financial report. It probably showed a poor trading result and he had come down here to let off steam about it. He relaxed. Quality wasn't the problem. A mild protest was in order. Neil respected a man who spoke up for himself.

"Wait a minute Neil. Our quality costs are normal, they are well within the predicted levels for this year and our technical quality really is good. Look, only this morning George agreed to delay a new product release because my engineers had found three potential safety hazards. If it's not right it doesn't get out. But what you're talking about is something quite different. If we're not making a profit it's either Roger's accountants got the budget forecasts wrong or Tony's marketing boys fouled up or his salesmen aren't selling enough volume or we've got the pricing structure wrong. Maybe it's a combination of those things but one thing's for sure, quality is not a problem. In fact that's what we sell on, quality. That's why our customers keep coming back, they know they can rely on us for good quality."

Neil listened. Ace card up his sleeve.

"We're not talking the same language Harold," he said. "That new product delay, how long will it take? How much will it cost? Three potential safety hazards? That's not quality. Yes, you found them, but they shouldn't have been there in the first place. That would be what I call quality, doing a job right, first time. And that's what we are not doing. That's exactly why we're not making a profit. We're wasting it."

As he spoke Neil felt himself succumbing to a deep sense of weariness. The issues were clouded again. The way ahead, which had seemed so clear was now rapidly disappearing. His own confidence was affected. He knew he was not in control, and worse, the issues involved were so ill defined that he had no clear picture of what it was he had to control. He had expected that talking to Harold would have enabled him to define those issues. Harold was his expert. Harold said quality was not a problem. Even so, Neil knew deep down that Harold was wrong. Quality was the problem. Maybe the terminology was at the root of the confusion. The word quality obviously did not conjure up the same concept in Harold as he himself understood it. He needed help, but not from Harold.

He had intended putting Harold in his place with the Grand Slam, the BNT telex. Instead he pushed it courteously across the table, placing it directly under Harold's nose. "These customers who keep coming back," he said, "Well, we've just lost BNT." He scraped his chair back and got up. "Photocopy the telex and give the original to Sylvia. Let her know the earliest date you'll be able to give me a report on the problems they've listed."

Harold's heart sank as he leafed through the multipage telex. He looked up as Neil spoke to him from the door. "And phone Jock. Tell him to get that vending machine fixed. It's just swindled me out of a coffee."

As Neil departed Harold picked up the phone. He pressed the buttons angrily. Why did everybody and his grandmother think they could leave all their cotton-pickin' problems with him? What did they think he was? Some sort of magician or something?

Fuming, waiting impatiently for somebody, anybody to answer the phone, Harold began to think vengeful thoughts about quitting, early retirement. That would show them. Neil thought he had quality problems? He'd have real quality problems if it weren't for the quality system, disastrous problems. Lawsuits, bankruptcy and jail. Why did nobody ever answer their telephone?

He dropped the phone back on its cradle, picked up the BNT telex and began scanning the pages sheet after sheet, all thoughts of quitting forgotten now as he locked on to the problem. His years of training and experience came into play. He knew how to handle this.

He got up and went to the open door of his office to see who was available. Dick. He'd do. "Dick," he called. "Get Sally to photocopy this telex urgently. Two copies, original back up to Neil's office. Tell Sally to tell Sylvia I'll have a first report ready for Neil by ten o'clock tomorrow. Then come and see me with the copies. We've got some analysis to do."

3 *"No problem's too big. What it needs is a big solution, and the will to do it."*

Neil knew he needed help, and solace. A place of peace and quiet, somebody to talk to, a calm presence, someone whose thoughts and judgements he valued.

He made his way through the personnel department and stopped outside the surgery, trusting to luck that Dr James would be in, and free. The door was ajar. Neil knocked, waited momentarily and went in.

The company's part-time doctor, Dr James, was a middle-aged, stern-faced man with short cropped red hair. He was sitting behind his desk immersed in a magazine when Neil entered. He put the magazine down and leaned forward, offering his hand in welcome.

"Hello, Neil. Nice to see you."

"Hello, Doctor. How are you?"

Dr James smiled.

"That should be my line," he said, making himself comfortable again in his chair. "But if you really want to know, I'm very well. Couldn't be fitter in fact. How are you?"

He cast a professional eye over Neil's face, noting the signs of strain and the lack of immediate response to his question. Casually, Dr James picked up the magazine from his desk and showed Neil the article he had been reading.

"Did you know," he said, "in a normal year in Africa, an average of four million children die from hunger, malnutrition or related causes."

Neil thought about it, his own problem still weighing heavily on him.

"Four million," he answered. "That's bad."

Dr James nodded, sadly, his heart beginning to ache as he thought about it himself.

"Four million individual human tragedies," he said, "in one continent alone. And on a planet which has more than enough capacity to feed the whole population."

"They shouldn't have kids." said Neil. "Not if they can't feed them. It's irresponsible."

Dr James shook his head. "You can't deny people the right to have children. No human being can deny another that basic right. And it isn't irresponsible in African society. In their conditions it's the only weapon they have to fight hunger and disease."

"I didn't say they should be denied the right to have kids," said Neil. "What they do is up to them. But they have to shoulder their own responsibilities. We all have to. If we don't we become dehumanized, to that extent belittled."

"What would you do, Neil," asked Dr James, "if you actually saw a child dying of hunger, and you were the only person who could help?"

"I'd do the obvious of course. Anybody would."

Dr James leaned towards him, eyes bright.

"So what's the difference? We know they're there, just a few thousand miles away, right now, this very minute, dying. Why don't we do something? Why do we let it keep on happening?"

"Because it's too big. The problem's too big for us."

"Baloney!" said Dr James, sitting back in his chair. "No problem's too big. What it needs is a big solution. It has to be tackled internationally. Look," he went on, warming to the subject, "When are we going to realize that we're all in the same boat? All human beings, all on this big boat, this planet earth, sharing it. When are we going to realize that we're all human beings, all part of the same family? That we have to care for each other, help each other. Nobody can be responsible just for himself Neil, it doesn't make sense. We're all dependent on each other. It's so obvious. You may be a good director, good at business, but without the farmers to grow food, you'd starve. Without lorry makers to distribute the food you'd starve. The continuation of human life is just one big process Neil, and we're all involved in it. We've got to learn how to control it. And it can be done. All it needs is the will to do it."

Dr James and Neil both sat in their chairs. Both quiet. Each thinking his own thoughts. The doctor angered by the stupidity of men, so slow to see the obvious; Neil reflecting on Dr James's words.

He was right, of course. A big problem demanded a big solution, world-wide, company-wide, it was all the same. No problem was too big to be solved. It was all one process, the continuation of human life or a straightforward profit-making organization, it was all one. And what was the other point Dr James had made? Responsibility? Interdependence? That was it. The solution was obvious. A bright clear shining path lay ahead of him.

Neil sat up and stretched his back, refreshed.

"Dr James," he said, "I wish you were on my management team."

Dr James smiled at him, dismissing the stupidity of men from his thoughts.

"I'm a doctor, not a businessman," he said. "There is one thing you could do though. Give me permission to start a regular fund-raising activity. Maybe we can't solve the international problem but we ought to do what we can. We could start collecting on a regular basis throughout the organiz- ation. Send the money to one of the famine relief charities."

Neil got up.

"Okay. You're on. Talk to Simone, in personnel. Tell her it's got my backing."

He turned round at the door.

"See you, Dr James," he said. "And, thanks."

Back in his own office Neil went immediately to his desk where a pile of papers, memos and opened letters awaited him. Without a glance he pushed them to one side, took his scratch pad and pen and set down the key stepping stones Dr James had illuminated for him. He wrote in block capitals

> BIG PROBLEM – BIG SOLUTION
> ONE ORGANIZATION – ONE PROCESS
> SHARED RESPONSIBILITY AND
>   INTERDEPENDENCE
> THE WILL TO DO IT

Neil put his pen down with a sigh of relief. His self- confidence had been restored; he knew where he was going, the direction he had to steer the ship. They were miles off course but that wasn't important. The ship itself was sturdily built, updated with all the benefits modern technology had to offer. The crew were undisciplined, disorganized, but they were willing, they could be trained.

Neil picked up his pen and added to the bottom of his list the word,

> TRAINING.

He put his pen down. Yes, they could be trained; everybody could be trained, nobody was beyond training. Even he, Neil, had to admit that he didn't know everything. Training was an essential part of the disciplines involved.

Knowing the job, understanding the process, confidence in the results, working together, sharing the responsibility.

Neil was fired with enthusiasm. He hadn't felt like this since his young years. A sense of excitement filled him. He knew the compass setting, the coordinates of the ship's destination. They were about to set out on a voyage of discovery in a sea of uncharted waters.

Neil smiled at the exuberance of his imagery. He leaned forward and pressed the intercom on his desk. Sylvia responded.

"Get me Piet van Oust, please, Sylvia. BNT, Geneva. And don't let them fob you off with anyone else. If they try, tell them I have to talk to Piet about his daughter, Angela. She's coming over here to work, to improve her English." Neil released the intercom switch and sat back. The day's mail was still waiting for his attention.

First things first. He felt in his coat pocket, pulled out his bank book and opened it on his desk. He wrote a cheque, hesitating after filling in the amount. He looked at the sum he had written and in his mind's eye saw himself walking past a little child with swollen belly, protruding bones, unnaturally big eyes. He growled internally at the stupidity of men that allowed such situations to exist and at Dr James for putting such a pervasive image into his mind. Angrily, he tore up the cheque he had just written, dropped the pieces into the waste bin, took his pen and made out another one, adding a zero to the figures. He put the cheque into an envelope and addressed it to Dr James, Surgery.

The intercom buzzed. Sylvia's voice came through. "Mr van Oust for you. I'm putting him through now." Neil stood up to take the call. Modern telecommunications had removed the need for a telephone in the hand and when the deep Dutch voice spoke it was as though the two men were in the same room together, electronically clean, crystal clear, perfect English.

"Hello, Neil. How are you?"

"Hello, Piet. Fine, thanks. How's the family?"

Neil listened, each topic for discussion clear in his mind, sequence and detail. A lot depended on this conversation, on his ability to convince a friend but still a hard-headed Dutchman, that he could put things right, change the organization, restore lost confidence. He had the will, the confidence; what he needed was the chance. Piet could arrange that if only Neil could convince him. And he could, he must. But later, family first, a job for Angela. Neil had no guilt feelings about this. He genuinely liked Piet and his family.

Regardless of the outcome he wanted to do his best for Piet's daughter while she was over here and he knew that Piet knew this. That was the degree of trust and mutual respect between the two men. Friendship was friendship but business was something entirely different. Business was hard, uncompromising. The rules were clear enough, relentless as the African sun. It was survival that was at stake.

4 *"What it means is, you're not in control."*

The following morning was a bright blue sky day, not a cloud in sight. Overnight rain had cleared the atmosphere and washed the biosphere, streets and houses, clean as a whistle. The brilliant sun did nothing to cheer Peter's spirits as he drove into work. Normally an early bird, his manufacturing background having accustomed him to rising at dawn, Peter was even earlier this morning. He had arranged for a manufacturing meeting to start at 8 o'clock. All his managers would be there, and hopefully with answers to certain questions which he had put to them the previous day.

The BNT telex had upset Peter more than any of his colleagues, more even than Neil, for Neil, like the others was worried and upset by the likely effect on the business. It was different for Peter. He took it personally. It was a matter of personal pride. He knew of course that he shouldn't take these matters personally; he even knew that in the end such a close personal identification with his work would destroy him, but he couldn't help it, he couldn't change. Peter envied his colleagues and friends their ability to distance themselves from real problems. It seemed to him that this indicated a bigger mentality, a maturity of manhood, this ability to concentrate only on the big picture and wave aside the elements of detail that caused him so much pain.

In reality he could see the big picture as clearly as any of them, and in fact it was precisely because of his awareness of the detail that his judgement, his assessment of the likely consequences of major changes, was the most trusted. It was to Peter that Neil turned whenever he was in doubt about a capital investment. It was to Peter that Simone turned whenever she had a pressing personnel problem. Tony came to him whenever he needed help in soothing an irate customer threatening legal action. All of them without exception trusted Peter's word implicitly. If Peter could help, he would. Whenever cracks appeared in the fabric of the big picture, Peter supplied the cement. He filled the gap. He helped others not for personal gratification but simply because that's the way he was built, he just couldn't help being helpful. But he couldn't help himself. He couldn't shake off a sense of failure, of personal responsibility when things went wrong. Things seemed to be going wrong more often as the years went by, he reflected, as he drove along the bright sun-lit road, houses drifting by on either side, washed clean by the earlier rain. A slower moving car was ahead of him. He checked his rear view mirror, pulled out and overtook, moved back into his own lane.

Each promotion at work had brought him a sense of achievement, more responsibility. He hadn't thought about it too deeply, just accepted it as a natural progression. The extra money was very welcome, the job was worth doing, he knew he could do it, in fact each advancement had been well within his capability. But life wasn't simple any more. He was not as much in control now as he had been when he was a section lead-hand. In hindsight the problems had started to escalate when he was promoted to departmental manager, but even then he had still been in full control. Now, as manufacturing director it was coming home to him more and more often that he hadn't a chance of controlling events any more. They were controlling him.

A uniformed figure appeared in the road ahead, waving urgently for him to stop. Peter, helpful as ever, pulled into the side of the road. Maybe there had been an accident, someone needed help. Strange, no vehicles in sight, no signs of help being needed.

Mystified, Peter wound down his window as the flat-capped man approached from the centre of the road.

"Did you know you were doing forty-seven miles an hour in a built up area sir?"

Realization struck him, a mixture of disbelief and guilt.

"Forty-seven?"

The police officer showed him the digital read-out on his hand-held radar.

"Forty-seven."

Peter groped for extenuating circumstances.

"I was just overtaking another car."

"Yes. She was doing thirty-two, sir. May I see your driver's licence?"

Peter sighed and gave in. He fished around in his pockets, found his licence, passed it across and listened attentively as the officer explained his options for payment while writing out the ticket. He gave it to Peter to sign, received it back from him, tore off the original and handed it back through the open window.

"This is also the receipt for your driver's licence. If you get stopped again just show it to them. Thank you, sir. Good morning."

The delay and the subsequently slower pace of travel as he completed the journey to work lost him the preparation time he had planned prior to attending the meeting. Instead of being mentally alert he was still suffering from a mixture of guilt feelings and annoyance at his own blindness when he walked into the conference room.

They were all there, all nine of them. Somebody had had the presence of mind to organize coffee. His was waiting for him. They were a good lot. Peter's weighty load began to lift; he was with friends. In their own way and in their individual disciplines they shared a sympathy of problems cheerfully and responsibly. Yes, they were a good lot. Together they could beat the world, and certainly the competition.

"Thanks for the coffee," he said, joining them at at the table. "Sorry I'm a bit late. I got caught in a radar trap."

Jim's face lit up. He smiled gleefully.

"Gerrard's Hill?"

"Yes, did you see him?"

"See him? He got me too. What speed were you doing?

"Forty-seven. You?"

"Forty-two."

Max delivered judgement on them.

"You both deserved to be stopped." Max travelled by bicycle. They passed the next few minutes swapping stories of brushes with the law as they finished their coffee, adjusting to the new day and to each other. They were well aware of the seriousness of the situation. Loss of the BNT orders would mean an inevitable cut-back in production, lost jobs, maybe even their own. Their present jocularity and good humour was not a reluctance to face up to the consequences. It was merely a necessary prelude to serious discussion, a necessary gathering together of mental reserves.

Peter pushed his empty coffee cup to one side and took out his papers from his briefcase.

"Okay," he said, "Let's get down to business. I trust you've had enough time to investigate these complaints from BNT. I've got to see Neil today with some answers, so we'd better get rolling." He sorted out one sheet of paper from the pile in front of him and gave it to Harry who was sitting next to him.

"Pass this to Max. It's my analysis of the situation. Max, take notes will you? Now, BNT have reported one hundred and fourteen instances of error. I've broken these down to thirty-four categories or types of error. We are responsible for forty of the faults, thirty-five per cent. In other words, there isn't much of a pattern. Our errors are nearly all one-offs whereas the commercial and accounts errors, seventy-four of them, fall into only eight categories."

"They caused most of the complaints though," said Harry defensively.

"Yes," Peter replied, "but theirs are systematic errors, which are always simpler to correct. When they're one-offs like ours it's more difficult. You don't know where or when the next one is going to occur. What it means is, you're not in control."

George, the quality controller, wasn't going to take that lying down. "Wait a minute," he protested, "let's put this BNT thing into perspective. It's forty errors we've made over six months, and that, when you look at the scale of shipments we've made to BNT, works out at 0.45 per cent. That's a pretty good batting average as far as I'm concerned. I think BNT are being very unfair about this. And why didn't they tell us they were monitoring our deliveries? It's a pretty sneaky thing to do, in my opinion. I bet there's an ulterior motive behind it."

Several of the managers round the table nodded their agreement, glad that George was on their side.

"What a stupid argument." said Peter, angrily. "There's no ulterior motive. BNT are operating on the Kanban principle. We know that. They told us at the outset. They simply cannot afford faulty shipments. And of course they're monitoring our deliveries. We do the same with our suppliers. And you heard me tell you there are one hundred and fourteen errors itemized on their telex, not forty. Your 0.45 per cent, George, is wrong. The figure is 1.2 per cent. That's a pretty lousy batting average as far as I'm concerned. It's lost us a major customer and it's lost us who knows how many jobs, because mark my words, there's bound to be a cut-back. It may even have lost us the whole game."

Tight-lipped, Peter glanced around the table, out-facing his managers.

"I haven't time for debates or conjecture. I need to know where we are going wrong and what we're doing about it. Harry. You start. We made four late deliveries. Why?"

Harry, production control, adjusted his glasses and looked down at his notes.

"Yes. In terms of days late we're looking at three days, nine, eleven and twenty-two days late in completion of shop order. In terms of cause, two were due to material shortages, one due to faulty material and one due to machine breakdown. It took us three weeks to get the machine fixed," he added, looking pointedly at Jock, plant maintenance.

Peter looked at Jock enquiringly. Jock spoke back to Harry. "By the time you raised a work request you'd already lost four days," he retorted. "And whoever filled it in didn't mark it as a priority job, so by the time we got to the machine you'd lost ten days already. Then we lost another week trying to get a replacement spindle from Japan. In the end we had to make one ourselves."

Peter looked back at Harry.

"Why didn't you sub-contract the job?"

"Because engineering had marked the planning sheet unsuitable for sub-contract. There's special job knowledge required. It's not a straightforward job."

"We could have sent an engineer to the sub-contractor, couldn't we?"

'It's not that easy, Peter. The engineers have their own jobs to do. They don't go out to sub-contractors."

"But you could have taken emergency action. And you didn't."

Harry held his tongue. This was one job out of several hundreds all on the go at the same time and he only had a crew of six to control them.

"We'll come back to that, later," said Peter. "What about the two material shortages? Was the planning wrong?"

"No, the planning was right. Purchasing fouled it up. There was nothing I could do."

"Did you talk to John about them?"

"We send a weekly shortage list to purchasing."

"Did you talk to him?"

"At the shortage meeting, yes. We discuss all the shortages."

"I see. What about the faulty material? How did it get through receiving inspection?"

George spoke up for Harry.

"It came from an approved supplier," he said, "so it went through without inspection. Straight into stores. That's the system."

"And when it was rejected in the shop it went on to the shortage list," said Peter.

"Yes."

"And got discussed at the weekly meeting, I suppose."

Harry was beginning to feel harassed. "That's the system, Peter. Don't blame me. I didn't set it up."

"One last question Harry, before we move on. How many jobs are late?"

"Not many."

"How many?"

"We don't plan for lateness, Peter. We plan for all jobs to be completed on time."

"So how many jobs do you get completed on time then?"

"About ninety-five per cent."

"Is that a guess, or do you know?"

"It's a good estimate."

"A guess, Harry. We'll come back to that later as well."

He glanced at his watch. Quarter to nine already.

"Let's move on," he said. "The next category is on packing. Four shipments damaged on arrival."

"I've investigated those," said George. "One was due to. . . ."

"Wait a minute," interrupted Peter. "Since when were you in charge of packing?"

"Well. . . ."

"Well, nothing. Let Max talk for himself. He's the supervisor."

Max looked crossly at George. That kind of help he didn't need.

"The packs weren't strong enough," he said, shortly. "Ever since we changed over to foam packing I've had nothing but complaints. It happens all the time."

"How many times, Max?"

"Well, it varies. Depends on the job."

"What jobs? Which items?"

"Well, certainly the four BNT complained about. It happens on others as well. I'm always getting on to engineering about it."

Peter raised his eyebrows questioningly at Mark, engineering manager.

"Well, Mark?"

"There's nothing wrong with the foam packing process. It's invariably the way it's applied that's wrong. There's a degree of skill involved and if you get it wrong cavities are produced and this of course weakens the walls."

"Have the operators been trained in the new process?"

"We trained Max and two of his men. That should have been sufficient."

Peter looked at Max. "Well?"

Max glowered. He didn't see why he should take the blame for something that wasn't his fault.

"We were doing all right with the old packing method," he said. "We didn't have all these problems then. Engineering recommended the changeover. I wasn't even consulted."

"Max!" Mark exclaimed. "You were in on it all the way. Right from the beginning. We've been over the costings with you, explained the reasoning behind the the changeover, shown you how to operate the process, explained the things to watch out for. What more do you want?"

"But you never listened to me," replied Max, vehemently. "The decision to change over was cut and dried long before you came to me about it. I warned you about the sort of problems we'd have but you wouldn't listen."

Mark heaved a sigh of exasperation and sat back in his chair. He looked at Peter with an expression that asked, what can you do with a man like that?

Peter's own face was unsympathetic.

"Get Karen to fix up a meeting later this week," he said, coldly. "This one will have to be resolved. And quickly."

He looked down at his notes and then to Robert, the assembly manager.

"The next five categories are down to you, Robert. Three shipments wrong assembly, three shipments incomplete assembly, one shipment wrong modification level, one shipment failed functional test, and one shipment, quote 'fell apart'."

Fully aware of the risk he was taking, George had to speak up.

"Let's be clear about one thing," he said. "When BNT refer to a shipment being rejected they mean they've had problems with some of them and therefore returned the whole lot to us. It doesn't mean the whole lot was faulty."

"I'll be coming to you in a minute, George. After Robert's had his say. Well, Robert?"

Robert had come well prepared, having distributed the necessary investigatory work among his supervisors on the previous day. Now he had nine pages of handwritten notes for reference plus the supporting documentation, all neatly collated and stapled for ease of handling. Robert was relaxed.

He had all the answers. Investigatory work was no stranger to the assembly department, they were well used to defending their backs.

"We've investigated all the rejects we're involved in," he said, "even those going back five and six months. I don't know whether you have time for me to go into the detail at this moment?"

"Just give me the headlines. I'll get the details from your monthly reports."

Robert nodded his understanding and began to reel off problem and cause starting at the top of his pile.

"One shipment wrong modification state, caused by production control not updating the drawings and planning sheets in time. Bert was off sick and we'd finished the job by the time he got the update to us."

"Why didn't you pull them back for rework?"

"I gave them a concession," said George. "It was only a minor modification."

"Did you get BNT's agreement?"

"It was a very minor modification, Peter."

"And a very costly error of judgement," Peter replied. "Carry on, Robert."

"One shipment failed test refers to a batch of sixty which were returned to us five months ago. On re-test we found three failures due to faulty components. Our records show nil failures at time of manufacture. They were all right when they left us."

"Go on."

"One shipment 'fell apart', was a full batch of one hundred and ten, caused by the engineering planning sheet specifying the wrong adhesive."

He delved into his pocket and produced two small plastic bottles, putting one of them on the table before showing them the other.

"That's what we were instructed to use," he said. "And this is what we should have used."

Mark reached across the table and took the small, inoffensive looking bottle. He peered closely at it before handing it back to Robert. "There's no wonder they all fell apart," he said caustically. "That adhesive is out of date. Its shelf life expired two years ago."

"This new one we found doesn't have a shelf life," said Robert calmly. "It avoids such problems."

"Rubbish. All adhesives have a shelf life."

Peter brought the interchange to a halt.

"How are adhesives controlled in assembly?"

"It's difficult," said Robert. "We've tried 'Do not use after' labels but they fall off."

"That one didn't," said Mark, indicating the one still in Robert's hand.

Robert ignored him.

"The biggest problem we have with adhesives is the way purchasing buy them in. That and the lack of stores control. Sometimes they are out of date even before they're issued."

Peter looked at his watch. He didn't have time for all this. He needed twenty minutes at least to put his thoughts together before seeing Neil.

"Robert," he said, "in a word. Incomplete shipments?"

"Kit shortages."

"And wrong assembly?"

"Wrong issues from component stores."

Peter moved on.

"George," he said. "How are all these errors getting through quality control?"

"You can't inspect quality into things, Peter. And please, please remember. We're only talking about small percentages. Our quality is really very good."

"Yes. So you keep telling me. Look, I'm going to wind this session up. I want a detailed report from each of you before the end of the day. Mark, you collect them and give me a summary report. That's all." He watched his managers file out, hangdog expressions on their faces.

There was no need for that, he thought, after they had gone. It wasn't their fault. It wasn't anybody's fault. Manufacturing life was just too complex today, expectations were too high, the impossible was being demanded. They weren't heroes, just ordinary men, himself included. Too much was being asked of them all.

Peter recognized the trap he was about to fall into. His rational mind took a grip on his emotions and imagination as he set himself the task of examining whether or not he really believed what he had been thinking. Perfection was being demanded. Was it really possible or was it an unachievable dream, something to aim for, a road to follow without end, no real destination? In a way George was right. Their quality was good, but relative to what? Industry standards? Who sets the norm? Sure, they could achieve near perfection but nobody would be prepared to pay the cost. It was a practical possibility, the space programme had shown that. Men walking on the moon! But look at the cost. They weren't in the same league.

The real problem, thought Peter, was the vast number of different elements involved in the business life of the organization. Controlling those elements required resources. Money was the key. Given an unlimited source of money any and every resource needed could be found and bought. Nobody had that kind of money. Investment was dependent on the turnover, which was limited and therefore the investment was limited, the resources were limited and consequently the achievement towards perfection was limited.

Peter knew very well that each of the problems his managers had brought out were solvable. They would be solved in fact because they had occurred. The worry was that each day brought new problems. Tomorrow and the day after and the day after that. New problems every day, problems which couldn't be solved because they hadn't occurred yet. Some of them would get out in shipments to customers, like BNT. It was inevitable.

Peter looked at his watch again. Ten to ten. At least he could face Neil and the others with more confidence now that he knew his own mind. Perfection was the road they should be following but given their limited resources the expectations should also be limited. The quality levels being achieved were all that could be expected. He wasn't happy with this conclusion but he had thought it through; he could defend his stance.

He got up. Time to go.

5 *"One common aim for everybody."*

"Is he in?" It was ten to ten. Harold had promised Neil his report by ten and Harold always kept his word. It was part of his training.

Sylvia continued typing. It was a letter to Jorge Gomez, Director of Purchasing Operations, BNT. Neil had dictated it to her first thing, hardly giving her time to take off her coat. It wasn't her fault she had been late. She was in a car pool, Philip's turn to drive. If he'd kept his attention on the road instead of chattering, stupid man, he would have seen the officer flagging them down. Still, it could have been worse. It was only a glancing blow after all. But the fuss he'd made! Anybody would think they'd almost killed him.

"Yes," she said, not looking up. "He's got a board meeting at ten."

"I know. He needs my report for his meeting. Shall I go through?"

"He's not to be disturbed."

"But he may want me to attend the meeting."

"No."

Sylvia stopped typing and swizzled round in her chair. She held out her hand.

"Give me the report, Harold. I'll make sure he gets it before ten. If he wants you, I'll give you a ring."

Reluctantly, Harold handed over his report. "Just make sure he gets it before ten, okay?"

"Yes, Harold."

In his office Neil was putting the finishing touches to an orderly progression of logic. He added a final one-liner on to the bottom of his crib sheet, sat back, and reviewed the orderliness of his work. He was satisfied. The logic was indisputable, the stepping stones were all in place.

He checked his watch. One minute to ten. Time to go. He pushed back his chair, got up and went to open the door to the outer office.

"That letter ready for signature yet, Sylvia?" he asked.

"Nearly."

"Bring it in as soon as it's finished please. We must catch the mid-day post."

"I could fax it across if you like."

Neil shook his head "Piet will need time to talk to Jorge. Just make sure it's in the twelve o'clock post. And could you organize coffee? Bring it in with the letter, please Syl."

Sylvia remembered Harold's report. She picked it up and handed it across to Neil.

"Harold said you wanted this for your meeting. And did you want him to attend?"

Neil didn't take the offering. "I'll read it afterwards. Tell him I'll see him this afternoon. Check my diary and fix a time, will you? Thanks." The door closed and Neil was gone.

Sylvia's finger tips ploughed the keyboard again. Coffee! What was she, a waitress or a professional secretary? She consoled herself by thinking of the satisfaction she could get from phoning Harold and telling him the boss wanted neither him nor his report at the meeting. But let him stew for a while. The anticipation would enable her to smile pleasantly when taking coffee into the board room.

There was a nervous tension in the room as Neil entered. He could sense it pervading the atmosphere like tobacco smoke. Tony, normally ebullient, full of stories and jokes, was silent, drumming with his fingers. Roger, glum, long-faced. Derek, normally alert, was leaning on the table, both hands propping up his chin. Fred, looking older than yesterday. Peter, calm, reliable Peter, with a sad, far-away expression on his face.

His team needed perking up, Neil decided. They'd had the stuffing knocked out of them. Needed a bit of backbone, an aim, a new direction. Fine. That's what he, Neil, was about to supply.

"Down to business," he said briskly, walking past his own chair and up to the flip chart which he had borrowed earlier from the training department. He remained standing, facing the table and set the tone of the session.

"This is going to be a short meeting" he announced. "I don't want any questions, no discussion at this stage, just your attention. Look on it as a briefing session rather than a meeting. But do listen carefully to what I have to say."

He picked up a red marker pen, wrote two words on the white sheet, replaced the pen on the ledge and turned to face his team.

"That's what it's all about," he said, pointing. "Profit

and customers; that's what we are here for and that's what we're not doing. We're not making a profit and we are not keeping our customers. That's the problem in a nutshell. It's a big problem, but we are going to crack it. There is no alternative, no other option."

Neil paused, letting his determination sink in "It's a big problem," he continued, "and big problems need big solutions. This is how we're going to do it." He turned back to the flip chart picked up the pen and drew a circle with several arrows outside, all pointing to the circumference. He wrote 'THE BEST' in large block capitals inside the circle, and repeated the same words on each arrow.

"That's the problem," he said, pointing to the circle, "and these arrows are you and me and everybody in the whole organization. We are each going to aim at becoming the best in our own jobs. One common aim for everybody, no matter what the job, whether it's sweeping the floor, operating a machine, typing a letter or managing a department, our declared aim is that we're going to do that job better than anybody else can possibly do it."

Neil paused, glanced quickly at the faces round the table. They were listening politely; there was no light as yet in their eyes. He continued.

"The situation we are currently in," he said, "is that people generally do not know their jobs well enough. There are too many errors, too much rework, too many things having to be done again. That's what is bleeding us dry, swallowing up the profits we should be making. And even then it doesn't work. Errors still get out to customers, losing us their goodwill and eventually their custom. That's the present situation. Now, remember yesterday's meeting? Everybody blaming everybody else?"

Neil turned to the flip chart again and drew a straight line with lots of little lines across it, like a railway track.

"Each individual job" he went on, "is part of a bigger whole. Somebody makes a mistake there," he said, pointing to a position on the line, "makes a problem for somebody else further up the line. And, from what you said yesterday, that's happening far too often. In other words, in the present situation it is considered normal, not unexpected. Well, we have to change. We have to become an organization in which mistakes, errors, faults, are abnormal. An organization in which we do not expect things to be wrong, an organization in which everybody is striving to be the best, not satisfied with second best, everybody striving for continuous improvement until they do in fact become the best. And even then going on and on improving, looking for ways to do a job better and better, continually striving for improvement. Continuous improvement in every part of our organization must become our way of life."

Neil was in full stream when someone knocked on the door and opened it. Sylvia came in carrying a trayful of coffee, smiling pleasantly.

"Ah, Sylvia," said Tony, pushing back his chair. "What a lovely smile. You're a sight for sore eyes, indeed you are."

He got up and took the tray from her, placing it on the table. Sylvia warmed, praise melting the smile such that it crept into her eyes. Maybe she'd let Harold down easily after all, she thought, taking the typed letter across to Neil for signature.

Peter sipped his coffee thoughtfully, reflecting on the similarity between the earlier board meeting and his own meeting of department managers. The same thing had happened, everybody blaming somebody else for causing their problems. It hadn't surprised him, it was part and parcel of manufacturing life. But maybe it wasn't inevitable, maybe it occurred because his own expectations were too low, maybe everybody's expectations were too low.

He looked at the flip chart, Neil's words catching his eyes. The Best. It was a grandiose aim, typical of Neil. He never did things in half measures. But that's all it was, an aim. Achieving it was a different kettle of fish entirely. Peter's mind surveyed the complexities of manufacturing life on the shop floor and he relapsed once again into gloom.

"Peter," Neil called, smiling over his coffee cup. "You don't look very happy. What's wrong?"

Peter sipped the hot coffee, considering his words before replying.

"It seems to me, Neil," he said, "that you're setting an impossible target. The quality levels we are achieving in manufacturing are as good as we're going to get. I can't ask them to give any more than they are already giving. Sure, I can tell them we're aiming to be the best. I can tell them we've got to improve until we are the best. But they're just words Neil. They'll want to know where the resources are coming from, because at the end of the day that's what it's really all about. Mistakes happen, errors of judgement are made, wrong assumptions are made. It's in the very nature of things, Neil. People are fallible."

"Exactly," Neil said, coming in swiftly as Peter paused for breath. "People are fallible indeed. We're all fallible, we all make mistakes and that's exactly why we have to focus on people as the solution to the problem. You mentioned resources. You've got the resources already. People. They are your resource. Look," Neil leaned forward intently, eyes alive with vision. "What do your people do when they come in to work? They come in to do a job, a boring old job for most of them. The same old routine day after day. Do they enjoy it? Do they look forward to coming in to work? No. For most people it's a matter of getting up on a morning and dragging off to work, something they have to do, not from choice. They have to do it to live." Neil held his hand up to stop Peter from interrupting.

"Yes, I know," he said. "I know it's not as simple as that. We've all been on these management training courses, we've all learned the various motivational theories that expound on human behaviour. What I'm saying is that we, as managers, haven't really tried to coordinate this vast resource of human creativity and abilities that is present in the people who make up our organization. In a way, we've seen and in fact we still do see, people as extensions of machines. With a job to do, just like a machine has a job to do. We've fixed the boundaries."

Neil got up, pointed to the railway track. "My job," he said "from there to there." He sat down again. "And that's where we've gone wrong, that's why sales and admin have dropped such almighty clangers. People haven't seen, we haven't seen, that every job is an extension of somebody else's job before it and after it. Okay, you might say that we have seen it, that we've planned for it, that our job as managers is to control that extension, make sure the overlaps are smooth and correct. But Peter, you know as well as I do, our business is so complex that it's now beyond the capabilities of any one person or group of people in any hierarchical structure to coordinate all the elements so perfectly that nothing ever goes wrong. Yes, we do it to a degree but we can't do it well enough. Nobody can. That's why management always gets the blame when things go wrong, because we try to do it, we see it as our responsibility, we organize things such that the manager is in control; we've given him that responsibility. We thought we could do it. And we do accomplish it, of course. But, as I said earlier, we don't do it well enough. Both profits and customers are pouring through the gap between our level of accomplishment and perfection. The wider the gap the more money and customers we lose. So. Back to your people coming in to work. Including us," he added, "you and me. Everybody, every single person in this organization. That's the resource, we are the resource. We're all in the same boat, we all depend on each other, every single person is vital to the success of the operation. It's no good getting part of it right, we've got to get it all right. We've got to be able to depend on each other, we've got to change the structure so that people don't fall over because they're leaning on the manager. We've got to get away from the boring old job routine and find a way of harnessing people's intelligence, their abilities, their creativity. Because you can't do it any longer on your own."

Neil paused, searched around the table. His enthusiasm had caught them, flickers of light gleamed in their eyes. He smiled and stood up to point at the flip chart.

"We're heading towards uncharted waters," he said confidently. "And there's our destination, The Best. Not second best, not even best in the continent. Best in the world. That's our destination. I'll be honest with you, I don't know how we will do it, but we will do it. Obviously, we are heading for a vast re-education programme. We are talking about a completely different way of working, a different way of managing the business. It's vast because everybody is affected. Nobody, and I do mean nobody, can be excluded. People will need educating in their own jobs; they'll need to understand that they are not doing a job in isolation, that each job is part of a process. They'll need to know the implications of what they're doing. They'll have to find the real needs of the process, what the next in line needs from them. And then, when they really know where they fit into the process, they'll be asked to search for ways of improving what they're doing, to think about what they're doing, find a better way of doing it, and then a better way and better still." He paused, shook his head. "There's no end to it. As each individual, each group, each department arrives at their own destination, best in the world, there will still be scope for improvement because quite frankly, it doesn't take much effort to become best in the world."

Neil sat down. His coffee was cold but he drank it anyway.

"How long is all this going to take?" asked Tony. "What time scales are you thinking of?"

"To a large extent that will be up to you," Neil replied. "Changing the whole organization around is going to take time. We won't accomplish it overnight. It will have to be a gradual change, but we must have a plan. I expect we'll learn from each other as we go along but we must plan out the overall strategy. However that's not for discussion at the moment, in fact none of it is open for discussion. You need time to think about it. I don't know what your diaries are like but this has top priority. We'll meet again at ten o'clock Friday to review your proposals, suggestions, ideas. Before concluding that meeting we will have a strategy, complete with time scales. So come prepared. Now, some good news before you go. Good news with a sting in the tail I might add. I phoned Piet van Oust and discussed the cancellation problem with him. Evidently it was our assessment of BNT as a bad commercial risk that proved too much for Gomez's pride. I promised Piet I would write personally to Gomez apologizing for the problems we have caused and assuring him of an immediate improvement which will be guaranteed at director level. So there's the sting. No more clangers on BNT, even if you have to check each consignment, each piece of paper yourselves. Piet will want my head on a plate if there are any further problems. And you can rest assured that the plate will be big enough for more heads than mine!"

Not knowing how long the board meeting would last Tony had cancelled all his morning engagements and now found himself with time to spare. There was no pressing business anyway, nothing really urgent.

He followed Peter into his office and sprawled into one of Peter's more comfortable chairs.

"What a relief," said Tony. "Neil getting round van Oust like that. Gomez is a real hard-nosed character. There's no way I could have sweet talked him into changing his mind. But, Neil, straight in. Over the guy's head, straight to the top. Mind you, last time I was in Geneva I got the impression that Gomez was after van Oust's job. There's no love lost between the two. Maybe that helped us, gave van Oust the chance to tweak Jorge's nose." He laughed. Peter didn't.

"What about the sting?" he asked. "Director level responsibility. It's okay for you. You don't have so many problems to sort out. There's no way I can guarantee one hundred per cent shipments. No way."

Tony smiled reassuringly.

"Don't look so worried, Pete. It's easy. Just concentrate on BNT. Put your best people onto it. Give 'em a bonus. Tell George he'll be the first to go if there are any more foulups."

"Don't be facetious. You don't mean that."

"Oh yes I do. Why not? That's the guy's job, isn't it? Controlling quality. Tell him to put all his inspectors onto BNT jobs."

"And what about all the others?"

Tony shrugged.

"Which block is your head on? So let the other jobs suffer. You're not superman, Pete. Remember what Neil said about responsibility? Control? People leaning on the manager? He knows what it's all about. D'you know, I really admire that man. He's a hard-headed visionary is our Neil. Who else would go for the top like he does? Best in the world. What an aim. And he's right too. Everything he said made sense. Good, sound, common sense."

Peter was still worried about the hundred per cent guarantee Neil had promised. He knew it was an impossible promise. Neil shouldn't have made it. He shouldn't have put him on this tightrope with a noose around his neck.

"And what about those uncharted waters, Pete? Can't you just see it? We know the direction but there's no telling what we'll meet on the way."

Peter's rising irritation brimmed over.

"Tony," he said coldly, "I've got work to do. Disappear." Tony sat up in his chair. "Don't take it so serious, Pete," he said soothingly. "It's not that bad. Nobody really expects a hundred per cent. Not even Gomez. It was that clown in commercial putting BNT on the bad debtors' list, that's what really blew Gomez up. Look, I'm going over to Geneva soon. I'll find out what options Gomez has. One way or another I'll find out what the competition's deliveries are like. Then we'll know what we're up against. Okay?"

Peter sighed. Nobody could be mad at Tony for long.

"Tony. I know you're trying to be helpful, but you really don't understand. You've never worked in manufacturing. You don't know what it's like. Even in the best planned of operations the possibilities for failure are enormous, endless. You can't cover all the eventualities, it's impossible. Things do go wrong, every day things go wrong, and that's what manufacturing life is all about. Planning, doing, and reacting as quickly as possible when the unexpected occurs. Recovering the situation as best you can with a limited amount of money, time, materials, resources. And at the end of the day we still can't find all the things that have gone wrong. They're the ones that get out to customers. You can't stop it. Can't change it."

"Like that half-eaten pork pie in the BNT shipment?" Tony grinned. "Sorry Pete, I couldn't resist it."

Peter made a face and carried on.

"Now, Neil is right when he says that's where the profits are going. Not just in manufacturing of course. The same situation exists throughout the whole organization.

Admin, commercial, accounts, we're all in the same boat. And with that as the background, Neil goes and promises a hundred per cent guarantee to van Oust. It's impossible, Tony. We can't do it."

"Are you saying its impossible to improve?"

Peter shrugged.

"We can make marginal improvements, of course. We're doing that all the time. But not on the scale Neil's talking about. That's why I'm worried. If we lose BNT it will mean wholescale cut-backs. A quarter of the organization will have to go. That's a lot of people, Tony. A lot of families. And the hardest hit will be the manufacturing division. It always is."

"Well then," said Tony, "We've got to do it. You've said it yourself. It's improve in a big way or bust in a big way."

"But you've got to believe it's possible," said Peter, leaning forward on his desk. "You've got to believe it. And I don't, I can't. Thirty years in manufacturing tell me it's just not possible. I've done the lot, Tony. Machine shop, assembly, test, engineering, production control, management. You name it, I've done it. I know the problems first hand. I know what's involved. You can't control a business to that extent."

There was an intensity in Peter's voice that Tony found alarming, a side to Peter's character that he didn't recognize. Then it clicked. The guy's frightened, he thought. He thinks he's being asked for more than he can give. He's scared. Needs shaking out of it.

"Don't be such a schmuck, Peter," he said roughly. "What d'you think? It all depends on you? The rest of us don't have problems? Okay, so I've never worked in manufacturing. So what? You've never worked in sales. You think selling's easy? You don't know the half of it. It's a hard world out there, everybody trying to sell in a buyer's market. People know what they want and they know they can get it some place else if you can't supply on their terms. The customer sets the terms these days, Pete. It's no longer a take it or leave it situation. You don't know it, old son, but behind every sale there's a lot of hard work, a lot of dedication, team work, effort. Do you realize the countless hours of work that go into preparing quotations? And the quote's got to be right. Get any part wrong and you risk losing your shirt or your customer or both. And at the back of your mind you know you've only got a one in three chance that this quote you're slaving over will result in a sale. As for technical problems, you heard Roger and Fred moaning about the sales desks yesterday. They're right. I know we pass on problems. Some we catch, some we don't. And that's why I'm sold on Neil. Because he's got it in one. The only way out of this mess is to change our way of working. You and me both, all of us. My sales desks have got to know more about the commercial and admin set-up; they've got to know where they fit into the process, what's important to the next guy. We've got to stop treating people like children. We've got to change the environment, share the responsibilities, respect people's intelligence, encourage them to use their creativity. Don't be scared of it, Pete. Just think of the possibilities; they're endless. Everybody in the whole organization bringing their own talents to bear on the job. What an organization. What a set-up. It's a world beater."

A smile flickered across Peter's face. Tony had him half believing it was possible. A true salesman.

"Thanks Tony. I'll think about it."

"Think about it? You better believe it. You know the old adage, nine-tenths of selling is believing in your product. Believe in this, Pete and you're halfway there already."

He checked his watch and leapt to his feet.

"Look at the time! Sorry Pete, I've got to go. Duty calls. See you."

Tony whizzed out of the office leaving Peter to review the situation. He had a lot to think over.

6 *"The organization was rife with rumour."*

In the buying department the early spring sunshine flooded through the large picture windows, illuminating the quiet buzz of the open plan office. Telephones ringing, papers rustling, people working, talking, walking through the gangway, going about the day's business. Wearily, Selwyn reached for his in-tray and took another requisition from the top of the pile. He felt like death warmed up. Colic, the midwife had said. Most babies suffer from it. Nothing to worry about. Won't last long, just a few weeks.

A few weeks; it felt like years. Janet was coping all right though. That was a blessing. At least he could get away from the crying for a while. Wasn't easy for her, cooped up in a bed-sit all day. She deserved better than that. Maybe next year they'd have enough saved for a deposit. Or maybe sooner if he could get promotion. Not much chance of that though, no openings. Still, at least he had a job, a regular income.

"Hey, Sel. Heard the news?"

He turned round. Andy came closer, sat on the edge of his desk.

"What news?"

"They're going to shut us down."

"What d'you mean, shut us down?"

"Shut us down. Wind us up. I've heard the boss is going to make an announcement. We're losing so much money we've gone bust."

"Where'd you hear that?"

"Philip. He got it from admin. One of the blokes up there told him."

"And where'd he get it from?"

"I don't know. Sales ledger I suppose. They should know. We're going over the 'The Bell' at lunch time, find out more then. Coming?"

Selwyn shook his head.

"No. I can't afford it."

"Aw, come on Sel. I'll buy. You look like death warmed up. You need a drink."

Selwyn got to his feet.

"It can't be true," he said, "I'm going to check with Tom. Outfits like ours don't go bust. It's crazy."

Andy chewed on his mint. He was trying to stop smoking.

"Don't bring my name into it," he called as Selwyn headed for the supervisor's office. "I don't want to be accused of scare-mongering."

"George. What's all this about a shutdown?"

"Sorry?"

"The girls in assembly. They've been told we're all going to be made redundant because we've been making too many mistakes."

George took his glasses off and rubbed his eyes. As though he didn't have enough to do without being asked fool questions.

"What are you on about, Irene?"

"I've told you. Redundancies. We're all going to be made redundant. Is it true?"

"Course it's not true. Who's putting stupid rumours like that about?"

"I don't know, but it's all over assembly. There must be some truth in what they're saying. Everybody's talking about it."

George got up.

"Come on, Irene. I'll take you to see Robert. He'll put you in the picture."

"It's true then. We are going to be made redundant."

"No it isn't true. We've lost a big contract that's all. Come on. We'll go and see Robert. He'll fill you in."

"There's no smoke without fire, George," said Irene dolefully, following George as he weaved his way to the manager's office. "You mark my words. No smoke without fire."

The organization was rife with rumour. Like a forest fire it spread from mouth to mouth, distortions creeping in at every telling. Some were genuine misunderstandings, people passing on what they thought they had heard, some were outright fabrications, people wanting to out-tell the teller, and some were downright mischievous, from those who thrived on bad news; wanting to believe worse than the worst they lit new fires in the already blazing undergrowth.

Neil heard about it through Simone, personnel manager. She knocked on his door and breezed straight in, Sylvia having deserted her post for a few moments.

"I hear you've been given the push, Neil," she said. There were no preliminaries, no niceties by way of introduction with Simone.

"What?"

"You know. The silver handshake. Moved on to better things. Given the boot. Redundant. Sacked."

"Me?"

"You."

"Sit down Simone. You're making me nervous."

Simone stopped pacing the room and stood in front of his desk, both hands leaning on it.

"I've also heard that we've gone broke, we're bankrupt, that we're closing shop in three months' time, that an announcement of severe cut-backs is imminent, one-third of manufacturing is to be laid off and we've been bought out by a Japanese competitor."

"It's not true," said Neil. "He's a Korean."

Simone looked at him.

"Neil," she said warningly.

"Oh, none of it's true, of course. Where are these stories coming from?"

"All over the place. I've had three union reps one after another knocking on my door, each demanding an explanation. Wanting to know what's going on."

"And I trust you were able to calm their fears?"

"No. They want to see you."

Neil sighed. Of late it was just one thing after another.

"Simone," he said, courteously. "Would you mind not leaning on my desk. You're intimidating me. Go and sit down."

He waited till she was seated.

"Now," he explained. "We've had two items of bad news recently. The financial report and the near loss of a major customer. The financial situation I can handle, in fact it's already in hand. We are nowhere near broke; bankruptcy is not even on the horizon. As for the customer. You've heard of BNT? Yes, well, there was a problem which has now been resolved. No cut-backs, no redundancies, no lay-offs. Not now or in the foreseeable future. If the unions want to see me of course I will see them but I think it would be better handled by you. Rumours should not be given the prestige of denial from the top. What I suggest you do is, get a copy of the BNT telex from Sylvia and a copy of my letter to the purchasing director. Show them to the union reps; in fact you can give them copies of the telex, they should know about the problems we're having. My letter is confidential of course. They can read it, but no copies. The financial situation will be explained in my monthly report to employees and Roger will be talking about it at the next employee council meeting. There is nothing for them to worry about. Think you can handle it?"

Simone nodded.

"I just wish I'd been prepared before they pounced on me. It doesn't give a very good impression of management you know."

"Yes. I agree. I'm sorry about that Simone. Everything's happened so quickly. I don't know how those two items leaked out. People need to know what's going on but they need real information, not rumours. Anyway, if the reps still want to see me after you've talked to them, get Sylvia to make an appointment. Okay?"

Simone got up and headed for the door.

"Before you go, Simone, I've asked Sylvia to arrange a board meeting for later this week. Tie into it will you. There's a major policy change coming up and you'll be heavily involved."

She looked at him quizzically.

"All in good time, Simone. All in good time. It's not thought through yet. All I want you to do at this stage is to listen. But you'll be in at the beginning. Rest assured Simone, the future's looking bright for us, very bright indeed."

Simone closed the door quietly as though leaving an invalid's room. Sylvia was back at her desk. Simone paused and shook her head.

"Sometimes, Sylvia," she said, "I have real difficulty understanding men. He says I've to come to this board meeting you're arranging. What's on the agenda?"

"Improvement," Sylvia replied.

"Improvement? Well, we could certainly do with a good dose of that around here. Especially in communications."

7 *"He didn't want a navigation officer, he wanted a bomb-disposal squad."*

At two-thirty Neil made his way to Harold's office, keeping the appointment Sylvia had made for him. At the back of his mind he considered whether or not he had made a tactical error in the selection of venue. Should he have summoned Harold to his own office, let him do the walking? It wouldn't be fair to lead Harold on, into delusions of grandeur. Well, it was done now, and he needed the exercise anyway.

Trekking through the various departments he smiled and nodded to those who saw him pass by, giving confident reassurance that all was well. He, Neil, had not been sacked. He was here to stay. The ship was in good hands, his hands, and it would soon be brought round on a new course, headed for a golden destination.

At the coffee machine on the final approach to Harold's office he paused, hesitant. The machine had either been thoroughly cleaned or it was new. From the way it sparkled and gleamed, and from the little bits of protective plastic still adhering to the chromework Neil deduced it was new. He smiled, dug into his trouser pockets for a coin. The power of his word. It amazed him still. His slightest wish had merely to be expressed and it was obeyed. Without question. His position was like possessing the little green bottle which, ever since reading about it as a child, he had always wanted for his own. A slight rub on its mysterious green surface, that was all it took to summon up the deep chested voice which never failed to echo from its depths. "Your wish O master, is my command. I hear and I obey."

Smiling, Neil dropped a coin into the slot, pressed the appropriate buttons for coffee, white, no sugar and waited. And waited, his smile fading away. An odd noise, remarkably like a death rattle, emerged from his throat as he punched the coin return button. Nothing happened. The machine towered before him, immutable, immobile, dead. Neil was not given to tantrums but at that moment, frustrated by his inability to batter the machine to bits, his whole inclination was to jump up and down, stamp his feet in a frenzy of activity. He restrained himself, admitted defeat. Breathing heavily, he continued on his way to Harold's office.

Harold was standing at his open filing cabinet when Neil entered the office.

"Not be a minute, Neil," he said.

Neil sat down.

"That coffee machine," he said.

"Yes," said Harold cheerfully, continuing his search. "Glad you noticed it. It's a new one. Jock installed it this morning."

"I know it's new, but I've just been swindled again."

Harold found what he was looking for, noted the figures and closed the file.

"Ah," he said. "Well, it's not been commissioned yet."

"Would it hurt anybody to put a sign on it, 'Do not use. I am not yet commissioned'?"

Harold sighed. Reached for the phone.

"You want me to phone Jock again, don't you."

"No. I want you to put a sign on it. Over the coin slot." He held out his hand. Lead by example, he thought. "Give me a sheet of paper. I'll do it."

Harold did as he was bid, then went to the office door which Neil had left open. Who was available? Dick, busy at the computer.

"Dick," he called. "Got a minute?"

Dick hadn't. His brain was immersed in software. He came anyway. "Dick'll do it," said Harold, instinctively proving his efficiency, his managerial control. He held out his hand for the sign Neil had just written. Neil got up.

"No he won't," Neil growled. "That's half the trouble around here. Nobody does anything themselves any more. Get somebody else to do it, that seems to be the motto for today. Well. It's not good enough. It'll have to change. Who's got some sticky tape?"

As he waited for Neil to return Harold puzzled over the minor eruption. What was Neil mad about? It couldn't be the coffee machine. That was too trivial, merely an inconvenience which had served to focus his annoyance about something else. Still better be on the safe side. He reached under his desk and pulled out his own personal coffee maker.

Neil came back in and sat down. "I thought I'd

banned those," he said, watching Harold spoon ground coffee into the filter.

Harold shook his head. "No," he said. "It was kettles you banned. When you got the drinks machines in."

Neil thought about it. The industrial engineering manager had done a study on the inefficiencies and time losses due to tea making throughout the organization.

"Maybe it wasn't specified exactly, Harold, but the obvious implication was that all personal drink making equipment was banned. Putting machines in was part of the efficiency drive two years ago."

"That's just it, Neil. You've seen how efficient they are."

"And what did you do about it?"

"Complained to Jock a few times, then gave up. Vending machine maintenance doesn't figure very high on his list of priorities. That's understandable I think."

"So you found your own way around the problem. Bucked the system."

"There's a fair few percolators around, Neil," Harold protested, deciding it was time to spread it about a bit. "And kettles," he added.

"How come I haven't seen them?"

"I suppose you haven't looked," replied Harold, innocently. "Anyway, I expect they're kept out of the way, like mine. I keep it under my desk. Do you take sugar?"

Neil did a quick calculation. Fifty thousand down the drain. Plus the continued losses due to personal tea making and the additional electricity costs of firing up all the kettles. He reached one hundred thousand and stopped. Some efficiency drive that had turned out to be. Another black hole swallowing up his profits. How many others were there? He made a mental note to speak to the industrial engineering manager.

Harold poured coffee into two plastic vending machine cups. Neil watched him pour.

"I'm glad to see the machines are good for something," he said, dryly. "Maybe it would have been cheaper just to buy the cups."

Harold smiled, relieved by the calm, even tone of Neil's voice. He replied in kind, offering Neil a friendly word of advice.

"You can get your money back," he said helpfully. "The money you've lost in the machines. You just have to fill out a chit and take it down to plant maintenance. But don't go before ten o'clock, that's when the office opens. Don't leave it too late though, otherwise the queue gets too big."

More losses, thought Neil grimly. A secondary system to accommodate failure. Instead of curing the problem at source we evade the issue and confirm the error, living with it. And then we make matters worse by devising ways and means, costly ways and means, of accommodating the failure.

Neil began to seethe quietly, drawing a mental comparison between compound interest and compound losses. How many times was this happening, he wondered. How many more secondary systems were there? Were there even tertiary systems to accommodate failure of secondary systems? Where did it end?

Human ingenuity, he thought, there's plenty of human ingenuity all right. Misdirected human ingenuity.

"And where do I get a chit from?" he asked politely.

"Admin. Accounts department. Philip has them. It's on a specially designed form."

"I see. Just out of interest, how do you prove you've lost money in the machine?"

"Well, you don't. I mean, you can't, can you?"

"Not easily," Neil agreed. "But doesn't that encourage dishonesty in employees?"

Harold shrugged.

Neil changed tack.

"Where does the money come from to pay out all these people who queue up at the office?" he asked.

"Petty cash, I suppose."

Silently, Neil added Roger to his mental list. Yes, he'd fill a chit out. For a hundred thousand he'd fill a chit out. Neil drained his cup.

"Thank you Harold," he said. "That was very interesting. It wasn't what I came down to talk about though. Tell me, what's the quality like these days?"

A strong feeling of *déjà vu* put Harold instantly on the alert. He'd played this scene before. Better get it right this time.

"Pretty good," he said warily.

"Can you be a little more specific, Harold?"

Harold got up, went to his cabinet and pulled out a thick file entitled, 'Monthly Reports to the M.D.' He opened it at his most recent report to Neil and began to reel off the figures. Neil stopped him.

"Yes," he said. "I remember reading it."

"It's all there," said Harold, closing the file.

"No, it's not all there Harold. Production only

accounts for about one-quarter of the organization. What about the remaining three-quarters? What about sales? What's the error rate there? Admin, accounts, commercial, engineering, stores, purchasing, all the host of indirects? What's their quality like?"

"I'm not sure I know what you mean."

"Well, the BNT telex for instance. That analysis you did for me, and thanks, by the way. You must have worked pretty hard to get it done so quickly. If I remember correctly there were one hundred and fourteen items of complaint of which seventy-four were caused directly by the sales, commercial, admin and accounts departments. And the one which nearly killed us was the admin error, putting BNT on the bad debtors' list which in turn put an automatic stop on further shipments to Paris. That's what I mean by their quality, or rather, non-quality. Now, your monthly report, those lists of production results, errors, faults. I agree with you, they are pretty good. In percentage terms some of them are down in the parts per million. And so they should be when you look at the capital investment we've made in the plant. But, and mark this, Harold, they are no longer important. The fact that you can report on them means that they've been found and corrected. Again, your quality cost figures, no cause for complaint, but one error in admin almost cost us a third of our turnover. And it's not just one isolated error. There were seventy-four such errors in just six months' business with just one of our customers. They are the costly ones, Harold, the ones you can't report on because you haven't found them. And you haven't found them for the same reason as I haven't found those kettles and coffee percolators which you tell me are hidden all over the place. Because, like me, you haven't looked."

Neil picked up his plastic vending machine cup, found it empty, and passed it to Harold for refilling.

"Now," he said. "There are a few questions I want answering. First, why did you allow this whole situation to develop?"

Harold almost spilled the coffee. "Me?"

"You. You're the quality assurance manager aren't you?"

The plastic cup was getting too hot to hold on to. Harold passed it back to Neil.

"Just a minute, Neil," he protested. "I can't be held responsible for everything that happens in admin, sales, commercial and all the rest of them."

"I don't mean that," said Neil, patiently. "I mean

the BNT situation. Why did we have to wait for the whole thing to blow up? Why did we have to wait for Geneva to tell us what we were doing wrong? Why didn't you tell me what the situation was before it got to that stage?"

"Because I can't second-guess the future," said Harold shortly. He reached for his file again. "Look," he said. "Every month. Customer complaints analyses. Every month I tell you what's going on."

Neil took the file and scanned the six previous reports.

"No you don't," he said, passing the file back. "There's nothing in there about a half-eaten pork pie in a BNT shipment. Nothing about misdirected consignments, late deliveries, documentation failures, invoicing errors, part shipments, wrong quantities. Your reports are straightforward analyses of returned goods, production faults."

It was Harold's turn to be patient.

"I can't report on what I don't know," he said. "I haven't got a crystal ball."

"You don't need a crystal ball," Neil told him. "You just need to talk to people, find out what's going on. Find out what really matters to customers, find out what we're doing to them. The information is all here, Harold. It's all inside the organization already. We don't have to wait for things to blow up in my face. That's not what I pay you for."

Neil restrained himself. He lowered his voice. "Look," he said. "Every single one of those seventy-four errors was put right eventually. In order to be corrected they first had to be communicated by the finder, in this case BNT, to somebody in our organization. Right? Now, that somebody is more than likely several somebodies, in several different departments, depending on what the problem was in the first place. Granted, I don't hold you responsible for everything that happens but I do hold you responsible for letting me know what is happening, as and when it happens and before it blows up like BNT. How can I steer the ship if my navigation officer doesn't tell me about the iceberg dead ahead? You don't need a crystal ball Harold. You need radar."

Harold listened in silence. He felt like weeping. How could he possibly collate all the data coming into the organization? Daily it was coming in, hourly. All the different customer interfaces. How could he possibly tap into them all? He didn't even know who they were, most of them. He could find out, but then what? The quality assurance department was already overloaded. Safety checks, audits, corrective actions, data analyses, Neil didn't know the half of it. He didn't know what he was asking. Utterly impossible. He didn't want a navigation officer; he wanted a bomb-disposal squad.

"That's the first thing," said Neil. "The second thing I want to talk to you about is costs. Quality costs."

Harold held his hand up.

"Wait a minute. I don't report on them, I just give you the bottom line as I get it from accounts. They do the analysis. Prevention, assessment and failure costs. In detail."

"I know, I know. Don't be touchy, Harold. I'm not going to bite you. I just want to talk about what quality is costing us. You're my expert, aren't you? Well then. Give or take a few points, our quality costs have hovered around six per cent of turnover for years, right?

"Yes."

"And that's normal? For our industry, I mean."

"Yes. I do talk to other quality managers, at conferences and exhibitions."

"Okay. No need to be defensive. I'm not arguing with you Harold. Not yet. So, six per cent is normal. And I suppose that is comprised from the conventional costs, is it?"

Harold wasn't sure where this conversation was leading, but he knew there was nothing good in it for him. Neil had adopted the cat's role, and Harold knew who the mouse was.

"The items are all specified, Neil," he said carefully. "It's a very detailed report I get from accounts. Rework, scrap, inspection costs, equipment, calibration, customer returns. It's all there."

"No it isn't all there," said Neil. "It isn't all there at all. What about the huge cost of rework in the indirect areas? Admin, accounts, sales desks, commercial, and on and on. They don't report their rework, there isn't even a system to cover it. What about the costs resulting from loss of a customer's goodwill? And how much money are we losing in wasted materials? We don't know. There's such a lot we don't know, Harold, but what I do know is that your quality cost report is only the tip of the iceberg. Six per cent of turnover? Twenty per cent more like! So, with that in mind, who do you think should be accountable for losing the modest five per cent profit we're looking for?"

Their eyes locked. Harold conceded defeat. He pointed to his own chest.

"Me?" he asked.

"That's right," said Neil cheerfully. "The profits are being swallowed up by faults and rework, and you're the quality assurance manager, so you're accountable. And I've

got to have it back, Harold. I've got to have it back to pay out
to the shareholders otherwise there won't be any organization.
Not for long anyhow. Now, I've done a deal with Roger. All
square and above board. I won't bore you with the details but
it's a deal I can't repeat. We've got to make a profit in the
coming year, Harold, otherwise we're dead. All of us. We're
all in this together. We've got to have that five per cent profit
on sales and that means we've got to improve. We've got to
improve across the whole organization, not just production,
in fact least of all in production. The whole organization. That's
where the profit is being lost, okay? Right. Now, the third and
final thing I want to talk to you about should be simple
enough. Dead easy in fact. It's quality. And no tricks this time.
I mean, I'm not out to trip you up, or give you any work. At
least," Neil reflected, "I don't think so. We'll see how it
develops. Any coffee left in that jug?

"You know, Harold, I've never really liked that
word, quality. There's nothing definite about it, nothing positive. It has too many connotations, too many different mean-
ings. No," Neil mused, "I like the words I use to be precise,
incapable of being misunderstood. Words like profit. Now
there's a precise word for you. Profit. When I say the word,
profit, you know instantly what I mean. I know what I mean
and you know what I mean. There's not a shadow of doubt.
Perfect communication. Not like when you use the word
quality. Whenever that word is used it seems to me that
people's brains go into neutral. Mine does, yours does.
Remember the beginning of this conversation? I said to you
'What's the quality like these days?' and you replied 'pretty
good'. There you have it. A state of complete misunderstanding existed between us. At the end of the day we haven't
got any profit. Our modest five per cent which, after all, is not
too much to ask for, is being swallowed up in errors and
rework throughout the organization. So, what you should
have said, in answer to my question was, 'the quality these
days is pretty lousy', or words to that effect. You see, Harold?
Our communication level was nil. And all because I used the
word, 'quality' in my question. It's not definite enough. It's
imprecise. In fact, I'm thinking of banning its use in our organization altogether."

Harold was on safe ground at last. He was the
professional, Neil was a business man. He couldn't be expected
to know about such things.

"Quality has a very precise meaning, Neil," he
explained. "In engineering terms it is defined as the totality of
features and characteristics of a product or service that bear

on its ability to satisfy stated or implied needs. That's the International Standard definition."

Neil thought about it.

"I've got a need," he said. "The business has a need. We need to make at least five per cent profit. I've stated it often enough. How does your International Standard definition take care of that? We can't be expected to go on satisfying everybody else's needs, not when our own need for a modest five per cent profit isn't being satisfied."

"You're mixing things up deliberately. Confusing the issue. You asked me about the meaning of the word, quality, and I've just explained what it means. Now you're mixing it up with profit."

"Not me," said Neil calmly. "I'm not mixing them up. Quality and profit are inextricably bound together in every conceivable activity. And not only in our organization. It's a universal law, Harold. I didn't invent it. Quality and profit go hand in hand."

Harold fumed quietly. Neil had deliberately led him up the garden path. Away from solid ground and into a quagmire. Of course he was right. Even the International Standard recognized it. "Anyway," he said. "You can't ban the word 'quality'. There's nothing to replace it with."

"Oh yes there is."

"What?"

"Profit." Neil replied triumphantly. "How about if I scrap the quality assurance department and replace it with a profit assurance department. How about if I change your job title from quality assurance manager to profit assurance manager. Maybe that would change the emphasis somewhat. It might put the horse back where it should be, in front of the cart. At the very least Harold, it would stop the tail from wagging the dog, don't you agree?"

To Harold's professional mind the conversation had deteriorated to a nonsensical level. To Neil's business mind he was talking sound common sense. "I'll give it some more thought, Harold," he promised. "I promise you, I will give it serious thought. Now," he continued. "Now, about this word, quality. Refresh my memory. What was that definition you quoted? The Standard definition. Would you mind repeating it."

Deflated, and feeling peculiarly foolish, Harold requoted the text.

"Hm. Hardly the sort of words that would mean very much to the ordinary man or woman in the street, are they?"

"Education," said Harold. "We do run quality training courses you know. And they're quite extensive too."

"Yes. I know," Neil acknowledged mildly. "I pay for them. Shall we go out into the offices, Harold?" he asked. "Just you and me? We could ask a few of the commercial people or even the technical people for that matter. You know, the brainy ones with a Ph.D. Ask them what the word quality means. How many of them do you think would come up with your text book answer?"

It went through Harold's mind to reply, so what? What does it matter if the operational people don't know the meaning of the word, quality? What matters for them is to know how to accomplish it. To do it, reliably and consistently. Harold held his tongue.

"Yes, I agree with you," Neil agreed. "Not many, if any at all. So I think we've arrived at the conclusion that, to the ordinary man or woman in the organization, regardless of rank or station, excluding yourself of course, that definition is eminently forgettable."

Wisely, Harold nodded his agreement. What was the point of arguing?

"Now, you might ask, why is it so important for people to know the meaning of that one word, quality? At this stage Harold, I'm not going to answer that question. What I am going to do is to tell you that it is vitally important to the well-being of this organization that we do have a definition which is memorable, meaningful, and most of all capable of being easily understood. A definition that everybody can relate to in the course of their everyday jobs."

Harold heard a change of tone in Neil's voice. The man meant what he was saying. The mildness had gone.

"Of course," Neil added, "I'm not denigrating the professional meaning of the word. It is valid. The work your department does is essential. I know that. But now we need something else as well. We need a simple definition that everybody can understand."

Neil got up. Flexed his back and made to leave.

"Sylvia is arranging a board meeting within the next couple of days. Tell her I want you to be there. With your proposals, of course."

He paused at the door and looked back at Harold who was feverishly hunting for a pen to scribble down what he could remember of the topics Neil had covered before they escaped his brain entirely. "Thanks for the coffee," said Neil. "I don't know what the blend is but if you'd like to try Blue Mountain, ask Sylvia to give you some of mine."

Harold stared open-mouthed at the empty door for several seconds before resuming his search.

"Dick," he called. "Dick. Got a pen I can borrow?"

8 *"Improve the whole organization, everybody, everywhere. Impossible?"*

Dick's head was down, calculator on his desk, halfway through a probability plot when he heard the boss calling him through the mist of numbers filling his brain. He sighed, dropped the pencil he was chewing and deliberately delayed lifting up his head, waiting for the repeat call which he knew would come.

"Dick, can I borrow your pen?"

He sighed again, laboriously coaxing his brain out of the world of probable events back into the realities of another unreliable day.

"Your need is greater than mine," he said inaudibly. He got up and opened his desk drawer. From the selection of mangled pens resting in the tray he chose one which carried the least obvious signs of consumption and carried it into the office.

"Thanks," said Harold.

Harold stared momentarily at the shreds of plastic hanging from one end of the pen. Dick watched him examine it.

"Not easy to stop smoking, you know."

"I'll buy you some chewing gum. How many of these do you get through a day?"

Dick made to leave but Harold stopped him. "Don't go, Dick. Sit down. There's a couple of things I want to talk over with you."

Dick sat down, waiting quietly while Harold searched his memory cells for the key points in Neil's monologue. The last point Neil had made was easy enough to remember. It was stuck in his brain like a sore thumb. Harold wrote it down,

"A new definition for Quality."

Next, profit. That had figured very prominently with Neil. He seemed to be ultra-sensitive these days about money draining away, seeing errors and rework lurking around every corner. He certainly had a fixation about lost profits even to the extent of accusing him, Harold, of losing them. Unfair, that. Still, nothing to be gained from dwelling on it. Most likely it was a throw-away remark, not meant seriously. So, profit draining away and what did Neil want from him? A method for plugging the gaps? No, he'd said something about improvement, and not just in production. Improvement everywhere, the whole organization.

Harold put his head in his hands as the enormity of the task he had been set began to dawn on him. Improve the whole organization, everybody, everywhere. Impossible. No one person could do that. An utterly nonsensical task. Such a lunatic notion didn't even merit a listing of the reasons why it was impossible. He shuffled about on his chair, put pen to paper and wrote,

"Improve the whole organization."

Rising annoyance at the boss triggered a sudden release of adrenalin, sharpened his wits. What had been Neil's introductory topic? BNT. Yes, he'd even accused him, Harold, of doing the losing again. No, he hadn't. Almost, but not quite. He'd asked how come he, Harold, had allowed it to blow up without warning. Why had he had to wait for BNT Geneva to tell him what was going on in his own organization? That was it. He wanted him, Harold, to report on everything that was going on in the whole organization. Another lunatic assignment.

Harold threw the pen down in disgust and glared at Dick who was sitting quietly at the table in front of him, pensively chewing the cuticle of an index finger. Harold picked up the pen and wrote angrily,

"Report on the whole organization."

What did Neil think he was running, a clearing house? There was something else, what was it? Oh, yes. Phone Sylvia. Get an invite to this board meeting she was arranging. Better do that now while it was still fresh in his memory.

"Not be a minute, Dick," he said, picking up the phone and pressing the digits.

"Here," he added, passing across the piece of paper on which he had written the three topics for which Neil wanted proposals. "Write these on the whiteboard will you?"

Sylvia's line was engaged. Harold put the phone down. He watched Dick write the cryptic sentences on the board.

"Neil's been down to see me," he said. "He wants us to prepare proposals on those three topics for discussion at a board meeting I'll be attending. Now, by way of background there are two things you should know. First, it's not been a very good year financially. Profits are down, caused by excessive errors and rework everywhere. Second, we've lost a major customer account. BNT. Caused by some idiot putting them into the bad debtors' book."

"That's not how I heard it," Dick said. He placed the felt pen back on the ledge and sat down again.

"Oh?"

"Profits aren't down. They're just not up."

Harold shrugged.

"Same difference."

"And we haven't lost BNT. We nearly did but Neil rescued us."

"Where d'you hear that?"

"John. The union rep. He got it direct from Simone."

Harold did his best to hide his annoyance, mentally going over the words he would have with personnel.

"Yes. Well. That's good news. Right then, let's get on with it. Quality. We need a new definition."

"Why? What's wrong with the old one?"

"Neil wants one that everybody can understand, one they can relate to."

Dick thought about it.

"Can I have my pen back?" he asked.

"Use the whiteboard."

"I can't chew that," said Dick.

Harold picked up Dick's pen and lobbed it across. It bounced off the table and on to the floor. "Be serious, Dick. I've got to have these proposals drawn up for that board meeting."

"I'll be serious when I've got something to chew."

"If it's that difficult why don't you stop stopping? Go buy a packet of gum or something."

"Can't afford it anymore. Not on my salary."

Harold refused to be drawn into another interminable discussion on rates of pay.

"Quality," he said resolutely. "We need a new definition."

Dick re-emerged and sat down facing the whiteboard. He chewed his pen quietly.

"I can see what Neil means," he said finally. "Quality is a bit of a non-word. It changes its meaning, depends too much on the context it's used in, and who's using it."

"It isn't really a non-word," Harold objected. "The Standard definition is very precise."

"For our own work, yes," agreed Dick. "But how many people know the Standard definition? For most people quality is something they know they want and something they know is missing when it's not there."

"Okay. Write that word on the board, 'something'."

"Well, no. Quality isn't a thing, is it. It's more of a concept than a thing."

"Write that on the board as well," Harold told him. "Go on. Do as you're told."

Dick got up and wrote the two words. He stayed by the board thinking.

"What's the dictionary definition?" he asked.

"Good idea, Dick. Get the dictionary out. It's in the bookcase. Over there."

Dick slid back the glass panel and pulled out two volumes, a dictionary and a thesaurus. He passed them across to Harold. During the quiet moments that followed Dick took the opportunity to refresh his memory of the Standard definition and while Harold was still reading he went back to the board and wrote, satisfaction of needs.

"Degree of excellence," said Harold closing the books.

Dutifully, Dick made the addition on the board.

"What's higher than excellence?" Harold asked.

"Perfection."

"They're hard words," said Harold thoughtfully.

"Not many people think in terms of perfection or excellence."

Dick nodded wisely.

"Most of us just want to get the job done and out of the way so's we can get on with the next job and get that one out of the way, and so on."

"You make it sound like an obstacle course."

"It is, in a way. There's always a job to do ahead of you and you can't get on with it until you've done the one you're doing. Like me, I've got a probability plot to do and I can't get on with it because I'm in here helping you do your job."

"Don't you enjoy it?"

"Helping you?"

"No, your own job."

"Well, it has its moments. But, put it this way. If my number came up and I won a fortune I wouldn't be here. And neither would you."

"Yes I would. I enjoy my job."

"All the time?"

"Most of it, yes."

Dick chewed his pen.

"Maybe that's why I'm the boss and you're not," added Harold.

"Or maybe that's why you enjoy it, because you are the boss," Dick retorted. "Maybe what you enjoy is not the job but being the boss."

"That is the job, Dick."

"Oh? I thought your job was to manage the quality assurance activity. You know, like making sure the customer gets what he's paying for."

"Yes. And I do that by being the boss, working through others, arranging for things to happen, balancing constraints, resources, deciding the best options."

"Anybody can enjoy that kind of job. But there's a big difference between arranging for things to be done and actually doing them. The difference is one's enjoyable and the other isn't. For most people, managers apart, of course, work is just something we have to do. It boils down to a matter of selection. Like me. I'd rather be doing a probability plot than digging ditches. That's all."

"Remind me to send you on a management training course, Dick. How did we get side-tracked like this anyway?"

Dick shook his head. "We're not side-tracked," he said. "You want a definition of quality that most people can relate to. Quality is part of the job, it's the way you look at the job. Doesn't matter whether the job is doing a probability plot or managing a department, selling, buying or operating a machine. The quality of a job depends to a large extent on your attitude. Of course, you can't do a quality job without the proper tools. You wouldn't want a surgeon operating on you with blunt scissors. And you wouldn't want a dental surgeon to go any further up your head than your teeth. But the overriding factor is the guy's attitude to the job. If he's got the right attitude he'll make sure all the conditions are right before doing the job. And even if he doesn't have the necessary skill or training, if he's got the right attitude he'll make sure he checks with somebody who does know before finishing the job. Quality is all about attitudes."

"But you said earlier that for most people work is just a series of obstacles. Jobs that have to be done and got out of the way. That doesn't fit in with your argument."

"Yes, it does. Because if a person's got the right attitude he'll do a good quality job anyway regardless of obstacles. He can't help it. We all work to our own inbuilt standard of perfection. Trouble is it varies from person to person. To misquote the bard, some, like me, are born with a high standard, some achieve it, and some have to have it thrust upon them. That's why we have a job." he added.

"It's a very pessimistic outlook," said Harold. "You can't change people's attitudes. Not easily anyway."

"Ah," said Dick knowingly, "But there is a modifier."

"Modifier?"

"Yes. It's called satisfying the boss. If the boss has a high enough standard his people will work towards that standard. Most of us do know what's good for us! Of course, the corollary is true as well. If the boss has a low standard then the obvious happens except, remember, the boss's attitude is only a modifier. People like me with high inbuilt standards will still do a good quality job because that's the way we are, but people with low standards will be able to get away with it."

"I see. And where does the customer fit into your philosophy?"

"That's where you come in. That's the boss's part of the deal. The boss arranges for things to happen, organizes things, finds out what the customer needs and what the bloke needs to do the job properly, starts the ball rolling and follows it through. So a boss can have a low standard himself but if he's a good organizer he'll be carried by his own department so long as he pays attention to what the customer needs."

"And when the manager has a high standard he'll be carrying those in his department who have a low standard because they'll be working towards his higher standard."

"Right. You got it in one."

"I'm not sure this is getting us anywhere, but add it to the list anyway."

Dick looked at the board.

"What? All of it?"

"Attitudes," said Harold. "Just add, attitudes."

Harold pushed his chair back and reviewed the whiteboard.

"Try this," he said. "Quality is the degree of excellence by which we satisfy the needs of the customer."

"Not bad."

Harold paused, watching Dick write his words on to the board.

Dick stepped back and looked at the board, thinking.

"How about this," Dick said. "Quality is an attitude of mind."

Harold nodded. "Write it down."

The office was quiet, both examining the whiteboard, reviewing the results of their combined efforts.

"I think we deserve a coffee," said Dick, finally.

"The machine's out of action."

"I mean, real coffee. Filter"

Harold bent down behind his desk and came up with a two litre plastic bottle that had originally contained concentrated extract of orange.

"Fetch some water then," he said. "And on the way call in on Sylvia. Ask her for some of Neil's Blue Mountain coffee."

Dick looked at him.

"That's not on the way. Neil's office is miles off."

"It is if you go there first," said Harold. "Go on, I'll phone her, tell her you're coming." Dick exhaled noisily and left the office carrying the two litre orange juice bottle.

Harold reached for his telephone, smiling to himself. Dick had a lot to learn. He pressed Sylvia's digits and sat back, waiting. "Sylvia," he said. "Neil's asked you to arrange a board meeting. When is it?"

He listened.

"Because he wants me to attend," he replied.

"When? Just a minute, I'll check my diary. . . . No, I can't make it. I've got another meeting. How about next Monday? I'm free all day . . . No I can't cancel it. It's not my meeting . . .. Oh, all right. I'll see what I can do. . . . What?. . . . Yes, all right. Book me in. I'll be there."

Harold sighed noisily. The power behind the throne. How had things got so reversed, he wondered. How had it come about that secretaries were now the real power in the organization? Everything revolving around their wishes instead of the managers'?

He looked across the table and located Dick's mangled pen. "Just a minute." He laid the handset on his desk, got up and fetched Dick's pen, returning to scribble out his previous engagement and enter the board meeting. He picked up the telephone and spoke into it.

"Sylvia," he said.

The line bleeped back at him.

Restraining his annoyance Harold cancelled the line and repressed the buttons.

"Sylvia," he said allowing just enough irritation to seep down the line. "I hadn't finished. There was something else. Dick's on his way up to you. Can you give him some of Neil's Blue Mountain coffee please?. . . . Because Neil said I could have some. . . . Yes. Check with him if you like. . . .

well, check with him when he comes back then. . . . Thank you, Sylvia. That's very kind. . . . Oh, all right. It's very kind of Neil then. 'Bye." He pressed the cancel call switch but not before hearing a click through the earpiece. Sylvia had beaten him to it again.

He replaced the handset. What next? Better try and get John to rearrange his meeting. He wasn't going to like that, not with eight people to contact.

Harold was still on the phone when Dick came back into the office with a full water bottle and a king size packet of ground coffee. Harold put the phone down. So much for that.

"You must be well in," Dick said, looking at the king size packet before handing it over.

Harold was surprised too. From the whole tone of his conversation with Sylvia he had expected a meagre couple of spoonsful. "You just have to know how to handle people, Dick," he said, taking a fresh filter paper out of his desk drawer.

"Now, let's get back to work." Re-setting his percolator he looked up and checked the board for his next task.

" 'Improve the whole organization'," he said.

"That shouldn't take you long," said Dick.

"Not me Dick. Us."

"And how many of us are there?"

"We'll come back to that one. Maybe we'll get some ideas while we're looking at the other task. 'Report on the whole organization'."

Dick chuckled. "You don't half get some jobs, Harold," he said. "That one should keep you busy for a while. Like, next Christmas."

"Don't laugh too loud, Dick. You'll be getting your share of all this. And Neil doesn't mean a one-off report. He want's to be kept up to date on everything that's happening. Everywhere."

"His brain isn't big enough. You'd need a Eureka system to hold it all."

"That's good, Dick. Put it on the board."

"Put what on the board?"

"Eureka system."

"I was only kidding."

"Put it on the board. You're living in the modern world Dick, computerization. Real-time data terminals, everywhere, every bench, every desk. Interrogation facilities in every manager's office. Especially mine. Do you know who's king these days Dick?"

"Tell me."

"The one who's got the information. I'll let you into a management secret, Dick. You don't have to know it all to be acknowledged as an expert. You just need to know a little bit more than the other fellow."

"And that makes you an expert?"

"That's right. Until you come up against somebody who knows a little bit more than you. Then he's the expert."

"How much do experts get paid?"

Harold ignored the question.

"And the next stage," he went on, "is a feedback system. Put that on the board, Dick. Feedback system. On-line control. The computer telling you where you're going wrong."

"That's a pessimistic outlook," Dick said, scribbling the words on the board. "And while we're waiting for this Eureka system how are you going to report on the whole organization?"

"I'm not. How can I? We're not plugged in to sales, admin, and all the rest. They don't report to me. And I don't want them reporting to me. I don't want to be accountable for their sins."

"Good for you, Harold. Let them account for their own sins."

Harold pointed to the board. "Accountability," he said. "Write it up. Whoever is responsible for an activity is also responsible for reporting on it. Individuals to managers, managers to senior managers, senior managers to directors and directors to Neil. There you are Dick. We've got the Eureka system already. Only, instead of chips we'll use people. That make you happy?"

"Coffee's ready," said Dick. "Mine's white with two sugars."

Harold nodded.

"I know," he said. "I know. You can pour it when you've written that on the board. Just draw a basic organogram underneath accountability. We'll know what it means."

Dick drew the structure on the whiteboard and when he got around to the coffee percolator he watched, intrigued as Harold opened his desk drawer and fished out two packets of powdered whitener and five sugar cubes.

"What else have you got in that drawer?" he asked.

"You'd be surprised," said Harold. "Would you like a biscuit?"

"Got any chocolate ones?"

Harold took out two chocolate biscuits and passed one to Dick.

"Now," he said. "What are we going to recommend they report and how do they report on it?"

"Results," said Dick. "The bottom line. That's all managers are interested in. Don't bore them with the detail."

"So what's different with our proposal then? They already get the results. There's nothing new in that."

"Oh yes there is," Dick said, warmly. "At the moment all they report on is the good things. We'll have them reporting on the bad things as well. Faults, errors, like they do in production. We'll get everybody to do their own analyses and be responsible for their own corrective actions."

"Hm. Quite a culture shock for the sales desks and accountants."

"Do you think they never make mistakes?"

"No." replied Harold. "I'm sure they do. Everybody does."

"But you never get to hear about them, do you? And if you don't know something is going wrong you can't do anything about it, can you? Only when some smart outfit like BNT monitors it and reports back. So let's start doing our own monitoring and get to the problems before the customer does."

Harold sipped his coffee and pointed to the board. "Write it up then," he said.

"And there's no reason why they shouldn't report in the same way as production," Dick added. "You don't want lots of words. They can use numbers. Numbers converted into graphs, then you'll be able to see the trends, whether results are improving or not. That will make the reporting easier to do as well as to read."

"Good," said Harold. "Put 'graphs' on the board."

Obedient as ever, Dick wrote, Graphs.

"Now, structure. Who's this 'you' you keep talking about? Me? I don't think that's what Neil really had in mind. Without a major increase in my resources," Harold went on, "it would be clearly impractical for the whole organization to report in to me."

"It wouldn't serve any useful purpose, either," Dick agreed, "It's the one who's going to use the information who needs the information. And let's face it, even in our department the only use we make of production information is to tell somebody else whether the process is okay or not. We don't actually change the process, do we?"

"No. That's not our responsibility."

"And we don't know enough about the processes anyway," Dick added. "We aren't the experts. The expert is, or should be, the one who's doing that part of the process. And since that's where the results originate he already knows whether or not the process needs changing. So it's a bit of a nonsense really, the erstwhile expert reporting upwards into the management structure. All that happens is the information either gets lost in the system or the management structure eventually comes down like a ton of bricks and tells the expert what he already knows."

"That's a very narrow way of looking at it, Dick. The manager obviously needs to know what's going on."

"I know I'm exaggerating," Dick conceded. "And I know it's not as simple as that, but the way things are at the moment the manager only needs to know so's he can keep the whole silly system going. I'm saying it's a silly system because all too often the manager is looking at the process from his own narrow point of view. You say that I've got a narrow outlook and I say so has management and that's where the most damage is done, because the manager isn't inside the process. He isn't where it's all happening."

"Why does everybody always blame management?" Harold asked, wearily. "You're as bad as everybody else, Dick. I really am going to send you on a training course. Look, the processes are too big, too complex these days for any manager to be inside them. He can't be here, there, and everywhere doing everything himself. He isn't Superman."

"Then why have we got a system that tries to make out he is?"

"Let's get off this subject," said Harold firmly. "We're talking about a reporting structure, not a management structure."

Dick refused to be side-tracked. He shook his head. "You can't talk about one without the other," he said equally firmly. "It's an information management structure we're really discussing."

Harold's ears pricked up. "That's good, Dick. I like that. Put it on the board."

Dick stood up.

"And don't get me wrong," he said, reaching for the felt-tip pen. "I didn't say the manager should be inside the process. I said it as a statement of fact, because that's how it is. The manager isn't on the spot, where it's all happening, and it's necessary to appreciate that because it influences the sort of information that needs to be collected and who gets what. What the manager needs is information that only he can act on, make those big decisions you keep talking about, find the resources the expert needs but can't provide because he doesn't have access to them."

"And the expert?"

"He needs a different sort of information. First of all he needs to really be an expert, so he needs information about the process. Then he needs to know what's going on inside the process, as it's happening, so's he can fine-tune it, improve it.

"You mean, the expert needs to know the results?"

"Yes. Not the big results. The little ones. And he needs to understand why he's getting them too. That's important."

"Process information. Big and little results," said Harold, pointing to the board. "Add them on."

Harold reveiwed the whiteboard, musing quietly to himself. People were fascinated by results. Football matches, cricket, darts, even bar billiards, keeping score was an essential part of the game, making the score visible added another dimension. Apart from what it did for the players, it allowed other people to get involved, feel part of it. At some stage, Harold thought, we'll have to find a way of displaying these results too. Display boards of some kind, to add visibility, improve motivation, grab people's interest.

He made a mental note to discuss the subject of display boards with Dick at some later date, before turning his attention back to the whiteboard.

"Okay," he said finally. "I think we've got enough on reportage. Let's get back to improvement. How are we going to do that?"

"Easy," said Dick, sitting down again. "It's got to be done locally. Experts and managers working together across the whole organization, solving their own problems, working as individuals, in teams, in groups, in whatever form it takes. The form will change depending on whatever it is that's being tackled."

The phone rang. Harold reached out for it. "Okay," he said. "Write it up, individuals, teams, groups. Hello?"

Dick got up and began to write as Harold listened to the caller.

"Dick," he said, covering up the mouthpiece with his free hand. "That probability plot you're doing for John. Have you got it finished yet?"

Dick turned and stared at him.

"No, I haven't got it finished yet," he said.

"Is there much to do on it?"

"Another forty minutes at least."

"How about ten?"

"No chance."

Harold took his hand away and spoke into the phone.

"Dick's working on it, John," he said. "He'll bring it up as soon as it's finished. . . . Sorry?. . . . No, he can't bring it up right now. It's not finished yet. . . . Well, you'll just have to delay your meeting. . . . About half an hour, forty minutes at most . . . Yes. Sorry about that, John. 'Bye." He put the phone down on its cradle. "One very annoyed project leader," he said. "Why didn't you tell me you were in the middle of a probability plot?"

"I did."

"You didn't say it was urgent though."

"Would it have made any difference?"

"Probably not."

"Maybe we should send project leaders on a training course," said Dick. "Teach 'em to do their own plots."

"Don't do yourself out of a job, Dick. Remember what I said about experts. Anyway, isn't it nice to feel wanted?"

"He doesn't want me," Dick replied. "He wants his probability plot."

Harold got up, stretched his legs.

"You'd better get on with it, then," he said. "And thanks for your input. I can tack a proposal together now that I've got something to work on."

Harold exercised his shoulders while reveiwing the cryptic words scribbled on the whiteboard, then went back to sit at his desk. He opened the drawer and took out a lined pad, settling down to write the three part proposal Neil wanted from him. He looked across the table and sighed.

"Dick," he called out. "Dick. Got a pen I can borrow?"

9 *"This whole organization is going to be turned upside down."*

Considering he was the sales director, Tony's office was small compared with the spacious premises occupied by other members of the board, but he wasn't sensitive about it. He was a warm-hearted man who liked people, liked to sense body heat, smell, the closeness of other human beings, so the smallness admirably suited his disposition. Colour scheme, dimensions, furniture, all combined to create a feeling of intimacy and comradeship which his intelligence told him was good for his occupation. Tony's philosophy was that selling was all about people, a basic philosophy which had never let him down.

Tony himself was a good salesman and he knew it. He was one of the best, with a long track record of successful deals behind him. He was also a realist, a major part of his achievement resting on his ability to size up a task and balance it with the amount of sales effort to be invested. This task, Neil's programme, loaded as it was with as many obstacles as there were people in the organization, was really going to take some selling. Tony acknowledged that Neil recognized this when he had mentioned the vast re-education programme, but he wasn't convinced that Neil fully appreciated how much support he was going to need. He couldn't go it alone; support had to be total for such a massive programme, and total support could only be given by people who believed in the product. Product belief was the power house, the driving force behind every successful campaign and for a campaign of the size Neil envisaged it would take much more than Neil, strong as he was, to drive it through. It would take all of them, the full executive team, and then more, and more.

He pulled a writing pad into position in front of him, picked up his pen and listed the names of the executive team: Derek, development executive; Peter, manufacturing; Fred, commercial; Roger, administration and himself, Tony. In his mind's eye he conjured up each in turn, starting with Derek. Conservative, a bit prim, very proper, not the type Tony would choose to be stuck in a lift with, but very good at his job. Clever, certainly knowledgeable but too highly critical if he hadn't invented it himself. Tony put a black cross against Derek's name and dismissed him. Derek wasn't the sort to be fired with enthusiasm by Neil's vision of an organization that was aiming to be best in the world, an organization in which creative freedom for every working individual was actively promoted in pursuit of this grand aim.

Peter, now. Good old Pete. Conscientious, hard working, helpful, reliable. A bit too self-contained for his own good, took things too seriously, although on reflection Tony had to admit it was this characteristic more than any other which had carried him through to his present position. Any task which Peter took on was brought to a successful conclusion, even those which were riddled with seemingly impossible demands. Unrealistic delivery promises made by his own sales desks, several came to mind as Tony thought about them, had been maintained in the end. Commitments without consultation, and yet Peter could be relied on somehow to achieve the impossible without losing the good-will of his own staff. If Peter took a job in hand he carried it through. But his reaction to Neil's proposal had been out of character. Why? Maybe they were all relying too heavily on him. Maybe he saw this as the last straw, one load too many. Or maybe it was the grandness of the vision, totally outside his experience, no prior knowledge to guide him. They were all in that situation, thought Tony. It had to be an act of faith or nothing at all. For his own good, Peter had to be convinced that it was the right path. Once he'd taken the first few steps he'd be able to apply himself, gain experience, confidence. Even maybe find that he could at last relax in his job as the weight of responsibility was progressively eased to its rightful owners. Good old helpful Peter, he needed his own hand holding now. Tony put a tick against Peter's name and moved on to Fred.

Fred was close to retirement but still putting all he'd got into the job. It was his generation, the way they'd been brought up. Vaguely, Tony's mind began to digress, saw himself at Fred's age and wondered how conscientious he himself would be when he reached near retirement. No chance, he thought. Life is more than work, more than the organization, especially when it's getting ready to cast you off like an old coat, out of fashion or worn out. But that was a long way off. Tony brought his attention back to Fred. He hadn't really reacted at all to Neil's message. Very defensive about the role of his staff in the BNT disaster but no perceptible reaction to the real issue. The more Tony thought about Fred in conjunction with Neil's vision the more convinced he was that Fred hadn't understood. He was intelligent enough to understand the words, but to understand the concept at a deeper level needed something more than Fred's upbringing had given him. There was a compensating factor though. Loyalty.

Tony smiled to himself. Not condescendingly, not dismissively, there was no sense of superiority in Tony's thoughts, more of a regretfulness at changing values. Loyalty was a rare commodity these days, loyalty to other than self. Loyalty today was justified only in so far as it coincided with one's own perceived needs. Fred was different. Come hell or high water Fred was loyal to the boss. Any boss. Fred believed in the hierarchical structure. From it came order, without it chaos. It wasn't the most solid of foundations on which to build a new structure but at least it was positive. Tony ticked Fred off.

Roger was next on his list. Roger, now there was a man totally dedicated to his profession. Not to his job; Roger was a chartered accountant first and foremost, a dedicated professional. His job, administration director, existed to support the practice of his profession. He delighted in it. Roger was a compulsive accountant.

Tony approached his assessment of Roger cautiously, knowing full well that he had a blind spot for professional experts. He didn't understand them, couldn't understand what made them tick. Instinctively he had a deep distrust of them, although this wasn't to say that he never made use of their knowledge. Whenever he needed further knowledge of detail or implication Tony always consulted the best. But then armed with the facts he formed his own judgement. Long ago Tony had come to the conclusion that it was their very dedication that made the dedicated professional vulnerable to error. They were tunnel-visioned people, blinkered workhorses. The errors of judgement which were made either by themselves or by those who relied on their judgement were not the small inconsequential errors. They were mostly cataclysmic errors, failings of nuclear proportions.

Tony made an almost physical effort and wrenched his mind away from Roger's grasp. He was biased. He knew it. He put a big black cross against Roger's name and switched over to the next on the list, himself.

He knew where he stood. No question about it. Neil's words had struck a chord so deep in his being that it reverberated again and again each time he recalled the vision.

The intensity of his reaction had surprised him just as much as Peter's out-of-character reaction had surprised him. And now, as he thought about it, Tony realized how jaded he had become with his own job. The years of experience had brought their reward but they had also taken their toll. There was no challenge any more. No, that was wrong. Tony corrected himself. It wasn't challenge he was seeking; there was after all plenty of challenge in increasing sales levels for the organization, further markets to invade, more inroads to be made on the competition.

The more Tony thought about it the more he realized that the reason for his submerged dissatisfaction was very similar to the cause of Peter's expressed concern. There was still ample challenge in his job but his years of experience had led him to the end of the road. Like Peter, he had recognized that there was no more mileage in carrying on with their old way of working. Even maintaining the status quo was becoming impossible. Deep down, he knew that he had begun to run out of answers. Neil's vision on the other hand presented a whole new ball game and more. It wasn't the aim that had caught Tony; it was Neil's vision of people working within the organization, an appreciation of the true value of people, the dignity of their human worth, the marshalling of talent and creativity, the freedom from restrictive practices imposed by outdated structures. 'Best in the world' wasn't so much an aim as the inevitable result for an organization which could achieve such a way of working together. Peter had linked the aim with the present way of working and had rightly concluded that it was an impossible target. He, Tony, had locked on to the vision of the new way of working. And he knew people, he knew it was possible. That was why his own reaction had been so intense. Neil's vision had opened new doors, a new way forward for everybody.

Tony gave himself two ticks and reviewed the list. There in front of him was Neil's first obstacle and maybe Neil himself was responsible for it being so formidable. He had approached them like a bull in a china shop.

On reflection he might have been better served by coaxing them along, seeding them with ideas, guiding them into his own way of thinking. But that wasn't Neil; his patience would never have lasted the course. The outcome from that process was never too sure anyway. Some people just could not be coaxed, but by the same token they couldn't believe in something by being told to believe in it either. Inner conviction, or belief, was an internal process, and woe betide the man who thought it was a simple process. Even he, Tony, knowledgeable and intuitive about people as he was, even he had never been able to unravel it.

There was the list, potential for support, potential for opposition, and worst of all, potential for sitting on the fence. Tony picked up his phone and rang Peter's number.

"Pete? Tony. What're you doing for lunch?"

Derek was last in. He threaded his way past four pairs of legs to a soft chair by the window.

"You should get yourself a bigger office, Tony."

"No thanks, Derek. This is plenty big enough for my kind of work. One of the basic rules of selling is that you don't let your customer get too far away from you. The further you let him get away the closer you let him get to the competition. A good salesman has to develop a customer mentality and you don't do that by distancing yourself from him."

"Thank you, Tony," said Derek, dryly. "I'll remember that little gem if ever I have to apply for a salesman's job. But I'm sure you didn't invite us for lunch in order to improve our selling technique. How about Neil? Is he coming over?"

"I didn't invite him. I thought we'd be able to talk more freely among ourselves without Neil."

To one side of the room a dropleaf round table had been furnished with a variety of filled rolls, a large jug of fresh orange juice and two flasks of coffee. Tony got up and took the role of host.

"This meeting on Friday," he said, handing out plates and serviettes. "Neil will be expecting us to be armed with proposals for putting his vision into practice."

"Dream, not vision," corrected Derek. "It's just a pipe-dream brought on by the financial results and the near loss of BNT. Don't encourage him down that road Tony. We're in enough trouble as it is."

"I used the word deliberately. It is vision, a grand vision of a future that could be ours."

"What? All that talk about uncharted waters?"

"The phraseology shouldn't bother you," Tony replied.

"That's what you're into isn't it? Research and development. You more than any of us should be familiar with operating in uncharted waters."

"That's quite different, and you know it. Technical development is based on proven fact, not fantasy. We don't go leaping off in the dark, chasing unproven theories."

"Maybe you should try it some time." Tony retorted.

"You might find a product that gives us a quantum leap ahead of the competition. But we're digressing. The rolls near my left hand are vegetarian," he said, offering the tray.

"I agree with you," said Fred. "It is a vision of the future and I trust Neil's assessment of the current situation. Neil is a remarkable businessman. Look how he got us out of that BNT mess."

"We're not out of it yet," said Peter. "We've just got a reprieve, that's all."

"But no financial reprieve," said Roger. "We're still not profit making."

Tony poured orange juice and handed it round. He filled his own plate with ham salad rolls then made himself comfortable in his armchair, listening to the voices ebb to and fro as his companions mulled over the current problems. He munched his rolls and enjoyed the orange juice, biding his time as he followed the conversation which had centred on BNT.

Fred summed it up. "No discipline these days," he pronounced. "People just will not do what they're told anymore. You can't rely on them."

Tony brushed fallen crumbs from his knees, got up and went to the table to pour coffee.

"There never was a time when people were reliable," he said. "Different motives, aims, ambitions, likes, dislikes, we're all different. That's what makes us so lovable; it doesn't make for reliability though. It makes everybody go scooting off in their own direction, including us. And that's what makes Neil's vision so attractive.

"Look," he went on, "what have we got at present? We've got no culture, no declared purpose. If we've got any common aim at all it's simply to survive in a tough world. That's no way to live, no way to work. Survival. What are we, a bunch of cave-men? But think about what Neil's offering. A real aim. Best in the world. That's no airy fairy ambition. It's something everybody can understand and it's a mite higher than mere survival."

Roger took a cup of coffee from the tray Tony was holding and helped himself to milk and sugar.

"I don't see how that gets us any further forward," he said. "Aiming to have the best organization in the world is just a grandiose dream."

"It is an organizational aim," Tony replied. "But the way of achieving it is for all of us to adopt that same aim as our own personal aim. All jobs, every single person in the organization, each of us aiming to be best in the world at our own jobs, at each task we take on, doing it better than anybody else can do it. And I for one believe that deep down that's what we all want, the self-respect that comes from doing a job as well as we can possibly do it. Don't you see? All those different motives, aims, ambitions, likes, dislikes. That one single, simple aim puts together the very differences between people which at present result in problems, and puts them to a constructive and unified use. It puts unity into the organization."

Tony bit his lip, thinking hard. It was so crystal clear to him.

"It's like," he said, "like putting a magnet to a piece of iron. Remember your school days, Roger? Remember scattering iron filings on a sheet of card and sticking a magnet underneath? Neil's aim is like that. It gives direction to people, pulls the present hodge-podge of aims, ambitions, abilities, all into line. And look at the strength of a magnet. Lifting up a car is no problem, but switch off the juice and, pow! No strength. If everybody takes Neil's aim to heart we'll all be pulling in the same direction. That's where our strength lies.

"Hmm," said Roger, not convinced.

"The 'if' is too big," said Derek.

"You got a smaller one?"

"No. But sometimes it's better to stay where you are if you aren't sure of the way forward. The problem I have with Neil's dream is that it's all based on motivating people into doing a better job. I'd rather see us aiming to develop a better structure, train people fully in the job and slot them into a properly organized structure."

"You weren't listening properly either. Neil's vision has nothing to do with motivational techniques. He was talking about the freedom of the individual to understand where his job fits into the local process, doing it better because that's the intelligent way to do it, and then looking for a better way still. Asking questions, finding out. Being creative, positive, instead of just trying to do what you're told when you haven't been told anywhere near enough to do the job properly in the first place. Neil was talking about a whole new way of managing the organization, Derek, not trying to motivate people into doing a better job."

"That gives me even more problems. I don't want Peter's production people putting their own changes into my designs. That is definitely not on. The risks are too high. Secondly, you've got a lot more faith in people's abilities than I have, and I don't see any reason why I should trust your judgement, or Neil's for that matter, rather than my own."

"I do."

"Yes?"

"He's the boss."

"Don't be naive, Tony."

Peter spoke up, annoyance putting an edge into his voice.

"Your designs aren't all that brilliant, Derek. Have you any idea how much drawing office effort goes into modifications? How much engineering time is spent resolving design problems on the shop floor? How often your development engineers are called into production? If it wasn't for production people putting thought and effort into your designs there wouldn't be much output from this place at all. The zero profit we're making would be a thumping great loss. And as for risks, no opportunity is without risks. Life itself is a risk."

That's m'boy Pete, thought Tony, get the old adrenalin flowing, you're halfway into Neil's vision already.

"Think about it Peter," Derek said sharply. "Everybody in manufacturing doing their own thing is utterly impractical as well as being downright hazardous. Even the simplest of design changes has to be controlled, evaluated for its implications. With the best will in the world an operator might change the length or type of an ordinary fixing screw with disastrous consequences. Every element of those designs has been carefully thought through and tested. Uncontrolled change would result in chaos. Think about it."

"You've got the wrong slant again Derek," Tony said calmly. "Neil's vision isn't about people doing their own thing willy nilly, uncontrolled. In fact, it's the exact opposite. Encouraging people to work together intelligently, inside the process, puts more control into it, not less. Of course design changes have got to be controlled, even the simplest. But surely there's a better way than the ponderous modification procedure you've got at present. It's up to you and Peter to work together and find it. Look, this is what we've got at the moment."

Using his index finger Tony described large circles in the air, naming each one as he closed the loop.

"Sales, accounts, admin, development, engineering, purchasing, stores, production, and so on and so on. All separate divisions and departments. We've even got circles within circles, departments within departments. In fact we've even got little groups inside the departments, one group supplying another group. And they've all got their boundary lines drawn up, little circles inside the bigger circles, all with their own rules, their own systems and codes of behaviour.

What Neil's vision does is to superimpose working links on to that structure." He drew long thin ovoids cutting through his imaginary circles.

"Working links of people, cutting across established boundaries."

"They already do that," said Derek, impatiently.

"Of course they do, people have always circumvented the system. But only when they have to, when something's gone wrong. It's nearly always after the fact, after the failure, after the event. What Neil is talking about is changing things such that it happens in a pre-planned orderly way, before the event, before the failure, so that the failure doesn't even happen and the work doesn't need to be done again because it's done right from a basis of true knowledge. Knowledge of what the process needs, what others need, to see the process through to the end customer."

Derek looked to Roger for support.

"Our problems go deeper than that. What do you say Roger?"

"Managers are not controlling their budgets properly," he said. "Stocks are too high, production planning isn't accurate enough. We're throwing money away on rework and scrap. The computerized system isn't working as well as they said it would. Yes, we've got problems and they wont go away of their own accord. I've been reading about Kanban, the just-in-time way of doing things. That would be a major step forward for us I think."

"We're looking into it" said Peter. "I've already got several engineers and production controllers being trained on it. But there's no way we can install Kanban into production in our present state. It would kill us. There's far too much uncertainty in our current ways of working. That's why we have all the buffers. If we try to run without them, we're dead. And anyway, Kanban will not solve the problems we're in, with BNT for example. No, I'm beginning to agree with Tony. We need a completely different approach, a new way of working together. I think Neil's ideas can do that for us, if only we can map out a plan of how to put them into effect."

Tony made one last attempt.

"Roger," he said. "All those things you mentioned, where we're losing money. They're all people-related problems. You're right when you said they won't go away on their own. But it's people who will have to make them go away. And by people I mean those who are doing the detail jobs inside those problems. Do you see the difference?"

Roger sighed. "I don't care who makes them go

away," he said plaintively, "so long as they don't keep cropping up on the wrong side of the accounts."

There was a small silence in Tony's office. Tony decided it was time to lay his cards on the table. "We've got a meeting on Friday with Neil," he said evenly. "I thought we should get together so that we could review the concept behind Neil's vision before preparing our individual proposals. That's what he's asked us for. Now, you can do something because you're told to do it or do something because you believe in it, and the outcome is as different as chalk to cheese. Belief itself is a powerful driving force. At the highest levels it's the most powerful force in the world. Some things need a passionate belief and that's the kind of driving force Neil's vision is going to need. He needs our commitment, plain and simple, and we can't give that commitment, that level of whole-hearted support without believing in the concept behind his vision. Neil's vision has got to be our vision too if it's going to succeed."

At the mention of the boss needing their commitment and support Fred began to nod emphatically. He didn't know exactly what was being asked of him other than that the boss needed his support. That was enough for Fred.

"Neil can count on me," he said grimly. "All he has to do is tell me what he wants from my division and I'll make sure it's done."

Tony didn't smile. Maybe in Fred's case belief in the boss was almost as good as belief in the principle.

"I'm sure Neil knows that, Fred."

Derek was quiet, staring intently at his fingernails.

"I'll need to think it through," said Peter. "It should be possible, if we can work out all the details."

Tony looked questioningly at Roger.

"I'll try anything," he said. "Anything that'll shift the balance into a healthy profitable position. Otherwise, we've got no future. None whatsoever."

"We've got a future all right," Tony promised, "This whole organization's going to be turned upside down and inside out. In a controlled way of course," he added, looking across at Derek, who continued examining his fingernails, expressionless. Tony shrugged and got up.

"Who'd like more coffee?" he asked. "Derek?"

10 *"Everybody is a supplier and a customer."*

Friday dawned. The day of reckoning. Neil tapped his pen on the boardroom table calling for their attention.

"This is going to be a crucial meeting" he announced. "Crucial for the whole organization. It will demand our full concentration, so please, no distractions, no wandering away from the points at issue. Before we start, and for the benefit of the regular members of the board, a word of explanation about Simone and Harold. Both are here without the benefit of being party to our previous discussions. I invited Simone because she will be heavily involved in two key aspects of our strategy, communication and training. Harold for the obvious implications on quality. Harold will also take notes of decisions and actions for distribution after the meeting, won't you Harold?"

Harold nodded mutely. It wasn't a task he enjoyed but it was one at which he was quite proficient. Sensibly he had picked up a note pad before leaving his office. Now he felt in his pockets for a pen. Surreptitiously he nudged Peter, sitting next to him.

"Peter," he whispered. "Got a pen I can borrow?"

While Harold was getting himself organized Neil gave a brief summary of their earlier discussions.

"So," he concluded. "The aims for this meeting are clear. One, to agree the concept and wording of our ultimate aim. The criteria being, first and foremost, it must meet the needs of the organization, it must be achievable and the wording must be such that every individual within the organization is able to identify with it and make it his or her own personal aim." Neil looked at Harold and pointed to the whiteboard.

"Summarize these on the board," he commanded. "I don't want anybody forgetting what we're here for." He glanced down at his notes.

"Two," he continued. "To agree the concept and wording of a new definition for quality. By giving top priority to quality, I am convinced that everything else will then fall into place. Output, timeliness, staff turnover, customer satisfaction, growth, profit, our own job satisfaction. All follow on the heels of quality. But we must be very careful in defining what we mean by quality. We must be precise in our selection of the concept and the words used to describe that concept. The concept must be published in words that are meaningful and easily understood by everybody. We cannot afford any misunderstanding or misinterpretation. It is imperative that we have a common language for all. For example, the concept of quality as conformance to specification is not adequate for us. It inhibits creativity, change, improvement, by implying that what is required is to slavishly follow a set of instructions. A specification can never be so perfect, written instructions can't be so comprehensive as to preclude the occurrence of error. Another example," he said. He looked across the table towards Harold who was standing obediently by the whiteboard, felt pen in hand.

"What's the Standard definition, Harold?" he asked.

Harold rattled it off.

"The totality of features and characteristics of a product or service that bear on its ability to satisfy stated or implied needs."

Neil nodded.

"That's the one. It's closer but the concept it expresses again is not adequate for our needs. Also, it's too wordy, too all-embracing. The concept we are looking for is one which puts people's abilities first. Because," Neil paused, looked around the table to make sure he had everybody's attention. He enunciated his next words clearly and slowly. "Because," he said, "quality is all about what people do. We need a simple definition for quality which puts people firmly into the picture. A definition which encourages them, gives them freedom to improve. Three," he went on, resuming his brisk no-nonsense tone. "To agree the strategy by which we will achieve our aim. So, first. The aim. You've had my thoughts, now it's your turn. Fred? You like to lead off?"

Fred's pleasure at being picked out by the boss showed on his face.

"Our aim is to be best in the world," he said. "It can't be beaten. It's an aim everybody can identify with while doing their job and the closer everybody gets to achieving it the closer the organization gets to being best in the world. I think we should stick with that."

"Do you think it's achievable?"

"It has to be," replied Fred. "Somebody has to be best in the world. Why shouldn't it be us?"

"Okay. How about you Roger?"

"Well, I'm not sure that being best will necessarily make us profitable. I can think of several companies that were renowned for their quality products and that didn't stop them going out of business."

"Be careful," said Tony. "Producing quality products doesn't mean that every task and decision taken is necessarily to that same high quality. Their products might have looked like world beaters but that obviously wasn't enough. To survive in today's world you've got to get the whole act right, not just the product. If you don't, if just one part falls down on quality, then the whole lot can collapse."

"We're not going to make the mistake of having a quality definition that's too narrow," said Neil. "Our definition must cover everything we do." He looked quizzically at Roger for his response.

"Fair enough," Roger replied. "So long as we keep profit at the forefront I'll go along with your aim."

Neil shook his head emphatically.

"No, you won't Roger, because profit will not be at the forefront. I have already said that quality will be at the forefront, leading us to the achievement of our aim. Profit will be one of the results of our working towards that aim but profit itself cannot be at the front end. Also, I don't want you merely going along with my aim. It has to be your aim as well, everybody's aim."

He looked around the table.

"I hope everybody understands that," he said, "because it's absolutely basic to this whole endeavour."

He turned back to Roger.

"Don't worry about the profit. That will come. I'm going to make sure it will come and before we leave this room I will explain exactly how I'm going to make sure, but the point at issue right now is the aim itself. So, back to you Roger. You've had two days to consider the proposition. What have you to offer?"

Roger sighed.

"I'd just like to keep it simple," he said plaintively. "Profit is such a simple word. Everybody knows what it means and everybody knows that we have to have it to stay in business. Why can't we be honest about it and simply say our aim is to make x per cent profit?"

"Anybody like to comment on Roger's proposal?" Neil asked.

"It satisfies the first criterion," replied Peter. "But it's far from being an aim everybody can identify with. In fact I'd go so far as to say nobody could identify with it, not even us, let alone people on the shop floor or offices. How could a girl doing an office job, typing say, how could she see her aim as being to make x per cent profit? How could anybody? No, I agree entirely with Fred. Organizationally and individually, to be best in the world is a real aim. I don't know how I as an individual would be able to measure my progress along that road but that's a different topic. I'm ready to accept the world beater aim for myself, my division and the organization."

"Me too," said Tony. "It has my whole-hearted support."

"Roger?"

"Okay. We can aim for it. Let's just make sure it doesn't cost us the earth getting there."

"Derek?"

Derek shrugged.

"No harm in aiming high," he conceded.

"We'll move on then," said Neil. "The quality definition. First I'd like to invite Harold to give us his thoughts on the matter. Harold?"

Harold left his post at the whiteboard and resumed his seat at the table where he could refer to his notes.

"Quality," he read, "is the degree of excellence by which we satisfy the needs of the customer."

"Write it up, Harold," Neil instructed. "On the board, where we can study it. Sounds good to me. I like the concept and the word 'excellence'. That's clever. Excellence, to excel, to be the best. It all fits in. Good. Well done Harold."

Harold glowed as he wrote the words in block capitals at the top of the whiteboard.

"The first part ties into the aim very neatly," Roger agreed, "but most people won't be able to relate to the second part of it. My people never see a customer and they don't know what his needs are. The same is true of Peter and Fred. Derek as well I suppose. How about changing it to, 'Quality is the degree of excellence we build into the job?'"

Neil thought about it.

"No," he said finally. "That would limit the concept back to product quality. Our definition must be one that everybody can use. Accountants and commercial people as well as production.

"That's easily solved," said Derek. "Change the word 'build' to 'put'. Quality is the degree of excellence we put into the job.'"

"That's still product-oriented," Tony said. "An accountant's tabulation or a sheet of typed paper is still a product. I think Harold's on the right lines there. He's got a people-oriented definition. Customers are people and quality is all about satisfying people. It's people who decide what they want, what they need. Every job we do is about satisfying people's needs somehow, isn't it? Nobody works in isolation."

Harold had a brain-wave.

"That's what I meant," he said, stretching the truth. "Everybody's got customers. Everybody who does a job passes it on to somebody else. That's what I meant by the term 'customer'. Not just the end customer. Everybody in the organization is the customer of whoever supplied him with what he needs to do his job."

Neil sensed something important coming up, an element vital to his strategy. He homed in on it.

"Everybody is a supplier and customer," he said, thinking out loud, seeing in his mind's eye the railway tracks he had drawn to represent the various processes which made up the total organization.

"Our aim is to be best in the world," he continued reflectively, "and to achieve that aim we must put quality first and foremost. By quality we mean the degree of excellence by which we satisfy the needs of the customer. And the customer is the person next in line. That's it," he said firmly. "Well done Harold. That's the definition we need."

"A minor modification though," Tony said. "Personalize the customer to the supplier and scrub the word 'needs'. Keep it simple. Quality is the degree of excellence by which we satisfy our customer. This concept of everybody being a supplier and a customer will have to be thoroughly explained to everybody though. It may sound obvious but it still requires a shift of perspective. Most people will see the customer as Roger did."

Neil pointed to the whiteboard.

"Harold," he said. "Change the quality definition to read, 'Quality is the degree of excellence by which we satisfy our customer.' Do we agree? Good. We stick with that then. Next point, Strategy for improvement. Everywhere and everybody. Harold, improvement relates directly to quality. I gave you the task of considering ways and means. What have you got for us?"

"There were two tasks involved," Harold reminded him. "Initially, they were quite separate and seemingly unrelated topics. Improvement and reporting. Improvement is needed to stop the profits draining away and since we're aiming to be best in the world we've obviously got to improve. Reporting is needed so that management doesn't ever get caught in another BNT situation. Now, the more I thought about these two topics the more I began to see that they are very closely interlinked. So, what I'm going to propose is a new information management system across the whole organization and then build the improvement process on top of that."

"We've already got a management information system," Derek said in a long-suffering tone of voice. "One that's been tried and proven over the years."

"Proven not to work," said Neil. "Carry on Harold."

Harold turned to the whiteboard.

"Information management," he said, writing it up. "Not management information, although as you will see the proposal will automatically serve that purpose as well. So, it's obvious that quality has to have a measure to be real, and it's equally obvious that improvement has to start from a known position. That's the sort of information which is needed, the sort of information which we've got to learn how to manage properly. Now, just as there are different levels of management so there are different levels of information. To keep it simple we'll have just two levels. One level for the manager who is outside the process and another level for the expert who is inside the process."

Neil's eyes gleamed. "Expert," he repeated, musing out loud again. "Degree of excellence, to excel, to be the expert, to be best in the world. Who exactly do you mean by the expert, Harold?"

"Everybody who is doing a job. Whoever is doing the job, he's the expert on that particular job."

"Sales desks? Typists? Accountants?"

"Yes."

"The person responsible for maintaining the coffee machines?"

"Him most of all."

"Hmm. Degree of excellence, to excel, to be the expert, to be best in the world. Yes. That's good. Very good. Carry on Harold."

Harold paused, collecting his thoughts. "So," he continued, "Two basic levels of information. The person doing the job must become the expert on that job, and to become the expert he needs information about the process. He needs to know what's going on inside the process as it's happening so that he can control it and then improve it. So the expert needs to know the fine detail of how the process works and what the results are. He also needs to be given the authority of an expert, the authority to change the process, fine-tune it if you like. The manager isn't on the spot, where it's all happening, so he doesn't need all that detail because he wouldn't do anything with it anyway. What the manager does need is the information that only he can act on. He has to find the resources the expert needs but can't provide because he doesn't have access to them. So, now we've got two levels of information and we've got the responsibility for acting on it. Whoever does an activity owns that activity and is responsible for reporting on it and improving it."

Peter looked dismayed, thinking of the mountains of paperwork that crossed his desk.

"Not more reports, Harold. Please."

Harold turned to the whiteboard and wrote a single word.

"Graphs," he said. "Not written reports. I haven't thought this through entirely but there can't be many activities where the output cannot be expressed in numbers."

"A typist," said Fred.

"The number of items returned due to typing errors," Harold replied. "Or the number of hours or days late in producing the typed copy."

"Switchboard," said Neil.

"Number of lost incoming calls per week, or number of seconds to connect an incoming call."

"Hmm. Go on, Harold. Continue."

"Okay. Now this information, these measurements or numbers will be made on key aspects of the process, whatever that process might be. They will be agreed with the customer who is next in line. Whatever is important to the customer, these are the measurements that will be made and reported by means of graphs."

"And the graphs can be displayed," said Neil. "Whenever I walk around the organization I can see what the results of any and every operation are. I'll be able to see the trends and I'll know whether that process is improving or not."

"That's right," Harold agreed. "But just as important, in fact more importantly, the person doing the job will know what the results are. And whatever action he or she takes to improve the process will show on the graph. It will be easy to see how far we are advancing towards becoming best in the world."

Peter interrupted.

"Just a minute," he said. "Don't you think it's asking

rather a lot? I mean, none of us are perfect. We all make mistakes of one kind or another, but asking people to display them for everybody to look at . . . . I can see that displaying results doesn't make them any worse, but how would you know they were honest?"

Neil looked to Harold for the answer but it was Tony who replied.

"That's up to us, Peter," he said. "As I see it, this whole programme is dependent on relationships, and not least the relationship between management and staff. If we're going to open the door for human ingenuity and creativity it will only flourish if the atmosphere is right. It's up to us to build a relationship based on trust and openness, where we're not afraid to admit our mistakes, but instead learn from them."

"Some of our managers are going to have to change their style," said Peter.

"Do you see a problem there?" asked Neil.

"Difficult to say at this stage," Peter replied. "But I think Tony's right. The initiative has to come from us."

"Well, no doubt we'll learn as we go along," said Neil. "Anybody else got any queries?"

He turned to Harold.

"Carry on, Harold. You're doing very well so far."

Harold beamed.

"Improvement," he said, confidently. "Not a lot to say about that really, except to say that I think it will have to be done locally. Experts and managers working together across the whole organization, solving their own problems working as individuals, in teams, in groups, in whatever form it takes. They'll need training of course, in such things as problem solving techniques, but on the whole I don't think you can produce a rule book for improvement. The form will change depending on whatever it is that is being tackled."

Harold searched quizzically around the table and then went to sit down.

"Thank you Harold," said Neil. "You've done well. Very well indeed. Draft up some notes on your proposals and issue them to the board. I think it's very close to what we are looking for. Any comments?"

"Sounds good to me," Tony said approvingly.

"Yes," said Peter. "Me too."

"Roger?"

Roger nodded thoughtfully. "Yes," he said, a hint of doubt clouding his assent.

"I can live with it," said Fred.

"I'll need to think about it," Derek said. "On the surface it sounds a reasonable proposition."

"Good," said Neil firmly. "Now we need a time-table, a plan for implementation. But first, coffee."

He pressed the intercom switch, calling Sylvia.

"Yes?"

"Coffee for eight please, Sylvia."

"It will have to be vending machine coffee."

"Why? Has my percolator broken down?"

"No. You've run out of coffee."

Neil frowned into the desk set. "What about that king size packet you bought on Monday?" he asked.

"Harold's got it."

"Harold? What are you doing giving my coffee to Harold?"

"He told me you said he could have it."

"Just a minute Sylvia."

Neil released the button and glowered down the table at Harold whose heart had been sinking throughout the conversation. Sylvia had engineered this. She'd done it deliberately. It would take too long to explain. He got up. "I'll go fetch it," he said.

Tony looked admiringly at Harold as he left the boardroom. Pinching the boss's coffee. The mind boggled. Who would have guessed he had the nerve?

Neil tapped the table, calling for their attention. "While we're waiting," he said, "we will continue our discussion. To summarize. One, we have defined the aim as an objective which fulfils the requirements of the organization and the individual. Two, we have agreed that quality will be our first priority and quality will be seen to be the road we are taking towards achieving our aim. Three, we have defined what we mean by quality in terms that lead us on to our strategy, our implementation plan. Four, our quality definition takes us into the supplier–customer–supplier concept, the concept of everyone being both a supplier to the next in line and a customer of those who supply him or her. Five, we have the elements of a strategy through the medium of quality performance measures or indicators in every department."

Neil changed over to his other hand to continue the count. "Six, we have the means of improvement through individuals, groups, teams, based on the customer's perception of where improvement is needed."

He paused, looked around the table.

"That is when the faults, errors, rework will begin to drop," he told them, beaming. "When people talk to each other, find out what their customers really need to continue their job and do it properly. Without mistakes. Find out how the process works, understand the process, improve it. Stop doing wasteful unnecessary jobs. That's when the money will cease draining away in wasted effort. That's when it will begin to mount up where it should be. In the profits column. And that's when we will be on our way to becoming best in the world. Well," he asked expectantly. "what have you to say?"

Roger's attention sharpened at the reference to a profits column. He responded promptly.

"We should begin immediately," he said. "Each day of delay is another day of lost profits, another day like yesterday. Our yesterdays are gone forever."

Tony looked at him.

"Such eloquence Roger," he said, smiling. "A poet's heart beats yet within thine accountant's money box. I agree with you. Whole-heartedly and with no reservations. Neil's vision shall be our vision, Neil's road shall be our road and whither Neil goes so go we."

Fred looked at Neil, wishing he could have said what was in his own heart as eloquently as Tony had expressed it.

"I agree," he said gruffly. "We should break camp as soon as possible and get on with it. Tell us what you want us to do Neil." Derek coughed.

"I think we should not get too carried away in a tide of enthusiasm," he said. "I recommend caution. We ought to test the concepts first. Try them out in an area which is already familiar with things like quality and measurement."

"You mean the manufacturing division, don't you?" said Peter.

"Yes. Why not?"

Neil answered the question.

"Because the profits are not being lost in manufacturing alone," he said brusquely. "There are icebergs in your own division Derek. Any one of them could sink us."

"My reaction," Peter said, "my instinctive reaction is that the whole thing makes good sound common sense. It feels right. In many instances we seem to have abandoned common sense and I for one would welcome a return to the principles and practice of common sense throughout the whole organization. Trust people, trust their judgement, encourage people to use their intuition, to apply their wit and skills properly. People want to do a good job, they want to give of their best. It's time we removed the restraints and it seems to me that's what this whole thing will do. It will change the whole culture of our organization. I think we should go ahead.

Start as soon as possible. And not just in the manufacturing division.

"Give me an example," Derek challenged. "What do you mean by our abandonment of common sense?"

Peter thought about it.

"Reports," he said. "Typed memoranda. Look at the number of sheets of paper that cross from one person to another, one department to another. Look at our costs for photocopying. Each sheet of paper takes time and money to produce, to distribute, time for the recipient to read, time and space for filing and so on. Is it all necessary? Or is it done for self-protection? Another one, costing. Is it common sense to have a costing and accounting system that concentrates on time sheets for direct operators in production? When their contribution constitutes the smallest element of our overall costs?"

"Is it common sense," Neil butted in, "to spend a small fortune installing vending machines with no maintenance programme to support them? Is it common sense that allows our best customer account to be entered in a bad debtors' book? Enough debate. We're going ahead. Simone. Thank you for being patient. I did ask you to sit in and listen and you've done that admirably. I hope you didn't find it too difficult. As you can see, we are faced with a major communications exercise. What do you recommend?"

The door to the board room opened and Harold came in carrying a tray full of china. Sylvia followed him with a jug of coffee.

"Saved by the bell, Simone," said Neil. "Thank you, Sylvia. That smells like real coffee. Pass the cream round, Harold. In your absence by the way we have agreed to go ahead. Starting immediately. Simone is about to give us her thoughts on the communications aspect. Simone?"

"We can't rush into this," she replied. "I'm not doubting the consensus of opinion expressed here and I'm not doubting the validity of the programme. But a major change like this needs detail planning. We will need to explain it to everybody, we will need to give the trade unions and the employee council time to consider the proposal and approve it."

"Just a minute, Simone," Neil warned. "This is not a proposal. It is not an option and it needs no further approval than this board meeting. Understand that, Simone. It is the future direction of this whole organization. No-one, and I mean no-one, can opt out."

Simone realized her error.

"I mean," she said, "people will need time to assimilate all this. It's a major change Neil. Bigger than anything we've ever done before. The implications are tremendous. We're talking about changing die-hard attitudes across the whole organization and at every level. You don't accomplish that overnight.

"I don't expect it to occur overnight Simone. I know it will take time, possibly even years, before it becomes a way of life. It will take effort and determination too. I'm aware of all that. I'm looking to you for guidance on how best to communicate the programme. Don't worry about the detail of what is to be communicated. We'll take care of that."

Simone was rarely lost for words. She demonstrated her quick-wittedness now, thinking through the logic as it developed.

"Trade unions and employee council," she said. "Separate meetings, two hours each, morning and afternoon."

"Why separate meetings?" Neil interrupted.

"Protocol."

Neil shook his head. "Protocol, custom and practice, tradition. No, Simone. We've got to break with old habits. One meeting. We will start as we mean to carry on."

Simone controlled herself. She nodded her acquiescence. "One meeting for the trade unions and employee council together," she agreed. "Followed immediately by an explanatory session for middle management."

"Why not one meeting for the lot? All together. It's the same information that will be given out. Why shouldn't they hear it together?"

"Because they'll have different questions. We're talking about a completely new way of managing the business, Neil. People are bound to be nervous. They'll want to know how it affects them. They will want to know what is expected of them. Some of the questions will very likely be directed at the very structure of management itself, sensitive questions, sensitive issues. I'm not prepared to answer questions like that with such a mixed audience."

"You won't have to," Neil replied calmly. "I will. I'll be leading the session. The whole board of management will be present. This is the dawn of a new future, Simone. Openness, honesty, trust and common sense, these are some of the values we must encourage and develop. We must be seen to be practising them ourselves if we expect to be believed."

Simone straightened herself in her chair.

"I don't know why you asked me for my recommendations," she said primly. "You seem to have got it all worked out already."

Neil relented. Unfair to expect her to respond so quickly. She needed time to sort out her thoughts. After all, the concepts were new to her. "I haven't got it all worked out," he confessed. "Just the beginning, the easy part. We've got the weekend coming up, a breathing space to work out the details. Think it through, Simone, and give me your recommendations first thing Monday morning. I'll want a time plan showing how you expect the programme to develop over the coming months, any special training requirements you anticipate, what communication media you'll expect to use, and so on. Don't worry too much about the detail. Just give me a broad brush picture. Harold, same for you. Monday morning, a draft of the concepts and method of implementation. We will announce the programme Tuesday morning. Simone, make the necessary arrangements please. Don't give too much away. Just say it's an extraordinary session with the board of management. I don't want anybody coming along with preconceived ill-informed ideas. Let the topic be new to them all."

"That's a fine way to start rumours," said Simone.

"Don't give them any background at all then," Neil replied. "Just tell them to be there."

"You were extolling the virtues of openness and honesty only a few minutes back," retorted Simone.

"Yes." he said. "But that doesn't mean an indiscriminate transmission of information. Discretion and honesty are quite compatible with each other."

Roger coughed. "One small question," he said nervously. "Where is the budget for all this? Who's going to pay for it? The training bill alone is likely to be rather enormous."

Neil's eyes gleamed.

"I'm glad you asked that, Roger," he said. "There will be no budget. No special provision. The whole programme will be self-financing."

He stared around the table, his gaze resting momentarily on each in turn.

"To put it in simple terms," he announced cheerfully. "You will be paying for it yourselves. Out of your existing budgets. Juggle them as you see fit. We all know how adept we can be at juggling budgets, don't we? And while we're on the subject of juggling, I'll tell you what I have decided to do about the missing profits, the profits I have to account for. Harold, nip next door and ask Sylvia for another jug of coffee. I think we're going to need it."

Harold got up smartly to order the coffee and Neil sat back, folding his arms. His whole expression said he was relishing this moment.

"At the beginning of the meeting," he said, "I deferred a query from Roger on the question of profits until we had concluded our discussions on the organizational aim and strategy for improvement. We have reached that conclusion, so I will now answer Roger's very proper question. Let me explain. We budget for materials, labour, covered reserves, maintenance of just about everything, except coffee machines of course. We budget for advertising, capital investment, and so on. The list is almost endless. We even budget for quality costs, the cost of appraisal, prevention and failure. We budget for failure," he repeated. "Rework, returns, and errors. It's true. Ask Harold. It's in his year end reports every year, but you probably haven't noticed. We budget for everything we can possibly think of, even failure. And at the end of the year when the final accounts are in and all the budgets accounted for, I have to be satisfied with the leftovers, usually nothing. Well, that's going to change, as of now. If we can budget for failure, we can budget for profit. We're going to have an additional budget, a profit budget. That way we will make absolutely sure that this organization ends each financial year with a healthy, profitable financial result. That should provide us with some motivation for improvement. It will also relieve me from being in the same embarrassing situation every year, explaining why we haven't made a profit and promising next year will be better."

Roger stared, aghast.

"You can't do that, Neil.

"I'm not going to do it, Roger. You are. You and your team of accountants."

"But you can't have a budget for profit when you haven't made any profit."

"A budget is planned spending, isn't it?"

"Yes."

"Well then. Our profit budget will be planned saving. Five per cent. Every month."

"But you haven't made any profit to save it. How can you put money in the bank before you've got it?"

"Roger," said Neil, impatiently. "You don't deal in money. You and your accountants deal in numbers. Budget numbers, cost numbers, balanced account numbers. We're going to have some numbers with the word profit on top of the column. And each month you're going to put a number into that column equal to five per cent on sales. You can work the other budgets from there."

Roger almost wailed.

"I can't. The rule book doesn't allow it."

"Then rewrite the rule book."

Tony was smiling broadly and openly. Fred lost in admiration. Harold came in with a fresh jug of coffee.

"Our voyage is just beginning," said Neil confidently. "There are exciting and challenging times ahead of us, I promise. Lots of rule books to be rewritten. Some we will just simply discard. Coffee, Roger? Or do you need something a little stronger?"

11 *"Enthusiasm, a sense of purpose, you don't generate those by pushing a piece of paper under somebody's nose."*

A cuddly grey blanket softened the Tuesday morning sky and eased people gently back into the workaday world of service, business, education and commerce. Another day.

Simone and her staff had worked late into the previous night producing photocopies of Neil's carefully worded announcement which was to be distributed to every member of the organization at noon on Tuesday. Simone's last job before leaving had been to place a large notice at each point of entry, ready to greet the arriving workforce in the morning.

There had been much agonizing throughout that Monday. Simone had produced her timetable of main events complete with a list of preparatory things that needed to be done in order to comply with the plan. With Dick's help over the weekend, Harold had clarified the strategy, putting detail and refinement into the measurement and reporting structure. Neil too had worked hard over the weekend, composing the words with which he would announce his vision to an unsuspecting organization.

All of this, the very backbone and fleshing out of Neil's initial vision, had been accepted with little or no discussion. The agonizing and interminable debate had centred on the approach and method to be used in starting out the programme. Should it open with a bang or a whimper? Derek urged caution. Neil favoured the big bang approach. Derek wanted to tread softly. Neil wanted sky rockets and a fanfare of trumpets. Derek pleaded for a lifeline, a safe haven in case a strategic retreat proved necessary, Neil demanded their boats be burned. Tony used his eloquence in support of Neil's approach. Roger, still reeling from Neil's revolutionary approach to budgets and profits, his soul still smarting from the wounds inflicted by Neil's incursion into the world of accountancy, nodded his head firmly in agreement each time Derek put forward an argument in favour of caution. Fred nodded wisely to support the boss and Peter just listened, weighing up the pros and cons until the main contestants had exhausted their claims and counter-claims. At the end, the calm voice of reason proclaimed Neil the winner.

"It's all or nothing, Derek," said Peter. "Everything in the programme is interdependent. We have to go all the way or we don't go at all."

Neil smiled. He would have won anyway, but better to win from a standpoint of reason and logic than to win because he was the boss. He could afford to be generous now.

"We'll follow your advice on staging the introductions Derek," he said, generously.

"We'll limit the first stage to an announcement of the organizational aim, the quality definition and the supplier–customer–supplier concept. When we've got those across and understood, firmly embedded in the culture, then we'll introduce the principle of quality performance indicators, the measurement and reporting structure and the improvement planning."

The session broke up shortly after Derek conceded defeat. Simone went off to organize the printed words that would be needed. Neil went into the training department to borrow their voice recorder. Harold went back to his office and called Dick in to explain some actions he, Harold, had been tasked with and which he, Harold, was now passing to Dick to accomplish. Roger returned to his desk to continue his search through the text books, looking in vain for a solution to the problem Neil had posed him. Derek went back to the security of his department and Fred was late for an appointment with his optician.

Tuesday dawned. The first arrivals yawned their way into work and stopped abruptly, clustering around the notices which had been erected by Simone the previous night. Eyelids pried open, brains put into gear, the new day began to take shape with increasing swiftness as they read the notice.

James read it out loud. "Please listen carefully to the public address system at eleven o'clock today when there will be an announcement which concerns everybody."

"Wonder what that's all about?"

"Sounds like trouble to me."

"Maybe somebody's got some good news for us."

"Fire practice, more like."

Simone, alert to the danger of fostering rumours, had made the notice as bland as possible, giving sufficient information to spice people's natural curiosity but pitched below the level which could possibly trigger alarm. The alternative approach which she had favoured would have been to prepare the ground by first distributing a copy of the typed announcement to everybody and then for Neil to follow up with his verbal announcement. But no. Neil wouldn't have it that way. His vision demanded impact. An address by the managing director would have impact, more than a sterile piece of paper. People deserved better than that. Simone was exasperated with him.

"Neil," she exclaimed. "You can't just suddenly pounce on people. You can't just suddenly make an announcement over the PA, out of the blue. People won't be expecting it. They won't be prepared. We have to prepare them. Give everybody a letter first, explaining the programme. At the end of the letter we can tell them you'll be explaining things more thoroughly over the PA, or better still, during your regular walk-abouts."

Neil was adamant.

"No," he said. "Announcement by letter would be too bland, too formal. And the walk-about idea is a non-starter, it would take far too long. We've got to stop pussy-footing around, stop treating adults like children. This whole programme, Simone, is totally dependent on people behaving like the mature adults they are and we can't expect people to behave like adults if we treat them like children, like eggs in a basket. That's got to stop. From now on we will be expecting people to deal with each other responsibly, in the way they would want to be dealt with themselves. And it starts here with us. Enthusiasm, Simone. Creativity. A renewed sense of joy at work. Vitality and vigour. A sense of purpose. You don't generate those by pushing a piece of paper under somebody's nose. They're human characteristics, like 'flu or measles. They're catching. They spread by human contact, person to person. You don't post them in an envelope."

Simone refused to be intimidated.

"People have got to be prepared," she repeated. "One way or another, they've got to be alerted to any announcement over the PA. It would be utterly irresponsible of us to catch them on the hop like that, out of the blue."

It was Neil's turn to be exasperated. "Stick a notice at each entry point then. Tell them to listen for an announcement at eleven o'clock. But don't give any indication of what it's about. I don't want to lose the initiative."

It worked. People were sufficiently alerted, curious to the level of healthy anticipation but not overly aroused to the point of alarm. Throughout the morning there was a lot of procrastination between work benches and desks, many interdepartmental telephone calls, much chatting up of friendly secretaries. The grapevine was thoroughly shaken that Tuesday as people ferreted for information but to no avail. The vine stayed bare as the hour continued its inexorable advance towards eleven o'clock.

Neil was alone in his office, waiting. In front of him was the audio-tape recorder he had borrowed from the training department. It contained his pre-recorded message and was already plugged into the public address system, ready to transmit his announcement of the new programme throughout the whole organization.

As he waited for the eleven o'clock deadline, Neil mentally reviewed the meeting he had just concluded. Simone had arranged things well, he thought, considering the short time-scales involved. He smiled, remembering the scene. At the front there had been the full board of management with himself in the middle, facing a packed audience of people who hadn't the least idea of what this was all about and certainly hadn't expected to walk into such a crowded conference room and be addressed by an imposing array of top management. The whole atmosphere had been charged with subdued excitement, keyed-up tension. This was the big one. It must be.

Neil had gathered himself together, collecting all his inner resources. Yes, he could handle it. He had stood up smiling, relaxed, open and friendly, confident and cheerful. "Good morning," he said. "Thank you for coming here at such short notice. I'll start off with a few introductions, just to make sure we all know who's here. Most of you will already know who I am, you see me often enough walking around the place, but for those who don't know me, my name is Neil Johnson, managing director of this organization and here we have the full board of management."

One by one Neil introduced them, by name and job function.

"In the audience," he continued, "there is, or should be, the employee representatives who are currently serving on the employee council, senior representatives from each of the trade and staff unions and last but not least the full team of managers from supervisors up to senior level managers. Now, in two hours' time, at eleven o'clock, I shall be making an announcement through the public address system. I'm using the PA because it's important that everybody gets to hear the message at the same time, apart from you, of course. You will be the first to hear the announcement because you are all in positions of extra responsibility and it is to you that people will come with their inevitable questions. So, what's it all about?"

Neil paused, allowing time for words to sink in, deliberately raising the tension. He had no notes for reference, he didn't want any. He knew what he wanted to say and his intuition told him it had to be said entirely ad lib. If he was going to convince the waiting audience of his sincerity and conviction his words had to be sincere, heartfelt.

"As of today," he said. "As of now, we, this whole organization, will be starting out on a new road. We will be starting on this new road together, from the same starting point, the same vantage point, and we will continue to advance together. No-one will be abandoned, no-one will get left behind. In fact, no-one will be allowed to be left behind."

The stepping stones appeared again, brighter and more visible, firmness and solidity built up from the depth of thought and planning which had occurred over the past few days. Neil launched himself into his vision, leaping nimbly from step to step, a logical progression of thought from concept to strategic approach, from strategy to planning for improvement, and from planning to doing. As the programme unfolded he returned again and again to the one aim, the organization's aim and the aim for each person in the organization. To be the best.

"It is not a pipe dream," he assured them. "Not pie in the sky. It is an achievable reality. Why? Because the world isn't populated with supermen, superwomen, people with superior intellects, abilities, people with unlimited resources at their finger tips, working in perfect organizations where everything happens in smooth and perfect harmony. No, the world is limited to people like ourselves, no better no worse, equipped along similar lines and operating within conventionally disorganized organizations. Whatever your job," he explained, "all you have to do to be the best is to do that job today and every day just one per cent better than anybody else. It is within your grasp, within your capability. By the simple medium of being a good internal supplier, being the best supplier in the world to the next in line, by paying real attention, not lip service, to the customer, the next in line, that is how we will build our organization into a real world beater."

Neil filled the whiteboard with diagrams. Circles pierced with arrows, 'the best' emblazoned in red ink, railway tracks to show job divisions and to explain the concepts of processes, supplier–customer–supplier relationships, job-knowledge expansion and the new definition for quality.

"Over the next few days," he told them, "over the coming weeks and months, we will be developing this programme of continuous improvement, this progression towards our aim and, as I said at the beginning, nobody will get left behind, nobody will be allowed to be left behind. We'll be helping each other, learning from each other and we'll not be afraid of making mistakes. No, we'll be open and honest about mistakes. We'll learn from them. As suppliers we'll be asking our internal customers to define their real needs so that we can understand exactly what is needed and then work towards supplying it. As customers we'll be telling our suppliers where they are going wrong, not critically but helpfully. Not bitching or moaning about things but calmly and constructively explaining why something is not right. In that way we'll help our suppliers to get it right. And remember, the customers and suppliers we're talking about are the internal ones, the next-in-line to you: by getting it right within the organization we'll be making sure that the external customers are being well and truly satisfied with our total service.

"We'll be helping each other as we go along, learning from each other, each one of us aiming to be the best supplier in the world in his or her own particular job. And as I've said already, nobody gets left out of this programme. It applies to everybody, each one of us going home at night knowing that we've done our job better than anybody else could have done it."

Neil held their attention for a full hour. Afterwards, during the thirty-minute slot allowed for questions, there were none of the potential problems which Simone had warned about. No embarrassing questions from managers or union representatives, no inhibitions, no smart alecs, just an intelligent and straightforward appreciation of the concepts, with the questions naturally being directed more toward the mechanics of the programme. John, the union representative, had seemed a bit sceptical at first, understandably nervous about the possibility of job losses resulting from the programme. Neil had reassured them all. No job losses, he said, will come from any improvement that is part of this programme. Of course, he had added, this could not be seen as an open-ended commitment; it couldn't be, not with the uncertainties of today's business world, the problem's outside our direct control like currency exchange rates and so on. But in so far as this programme was concerned, it would improve job security, not detract from it.

In his office, Neil switched back to the present and

looked at his watch to check the time. One minute to switch on. The start-up meeting had gone down well, at least that had been his own impression judging from the questions and comments he had received afterwards. He said a silent prayer that the public announcement he was about to make would go down equally as well.

Eleven o'clock. He switched the tape recorder into 'play' mode, sat back and listened as electrical signals fled from the magnetic tape pick-up, scurried down the telephone lines, into the exchange and out towards the loudspeakers which converted the signals magically back into Neil's pre-recorded voice. Anxiously at first, he kept track of his amplified voice against the hand-written script, which essentially followed the same lines as his ad lib talk at the earlier meeting. There were no electronic hiccups. He put the script down on his desk, picked up the cup of cold coffee and relaxed, listening and interpreting the sense of what was being said, trying to evaluate the common sense logic of the words as though they were as fresh and new to him as they would be to the people now listening.

Listening, Neil became more and more convinced that the programme on which they were about to embark was absolutely right in every sense of the word. It appealed to his intellect and humanity as well as his business and economic experience. He tried to put himself in the position of devil's advocate but could find no fault with the common sense logic, and instead became more and more certain that, compared with this, their present way of working was old fashioned and outmoded, out of tune with the spirit of the present age.

There is a time and tide in the affairs of men, he thought. How true. From the humanitarian point of view this was the hammer blow which would break the final link in the shackles with which Taylorism had for a while bound man's spirit. It would allow modern man to break out of the rigid robot mould fashioned by Taylor's production-line methods in the early years of industrialization. For the intellectual it enticed the application of reason back into a business world where the endeavours of the intellect had for so long been constrained by the application of non-reason. From a business and economic point of view it would release a wealth of fresh resources into every part of an organization in search of continuous improvement. Yes, he thought, both time and tide are right.

His coffee was cold. Noiselessly he got up and tiptoed into Sylvia's office. As he opened the door she looked round and put a finger to her lips, shushing him to be quiet.

That's a good sign, he thought. At least she's interested and absorbed. Let's hope the rest of the organization are just as interested. Neil reached his objective and refilled his cup before creeping back to his desk.

In the buying department Selwyn, along with every-body else in the office, was listening intently. This sounded good to Selwyn. Not only was his job safe, but it seemed like he was going to be given the opportunity to put some of his own ideas into practice as well. If he could show Tom that he was full of practical ideas to improve his own job maybe he'd get that promotion after all, bring that terrace cottage a little closer.

Syd was sitting back from his desk in the commercial department, pretending not to listen, pretending boredom. Best in the world? This outfit? That was a laugh.

Best in the world, thought Mary, sitting opposite Syd. Why not? Somebody has to be best, why not us? It would be nice to work in a place like that, where everybody did their job properly. And that internal customers idea sounded good too. It would be good to know that you were doing your job right and know that it was appreciated. The managing director sounded all right. She'd seen him plenty of times in the depart-ment, talking to people. Maybe now she'd get to meet him and judge for herself. Mary smiled. Well, she thought, miracles do happen sometimes, don't they?

Harry looked at the partially built assembly on his workbench, thinking about how it would affect him, thinking about what his day would be like, if only. If only the designers really were the best in the world, and the production engin-eers, the planners, buyers, stock controllers. No more designs that didn't need a fiddle to get them to work, no more tooling faults, no more shortages, no more faulty components, no more frustration. Harry sighed, looking at the partially built assembly on his bench. I'm everybody's customer, he thought. And all they give me is problems. If only they really would get their act together. And why not? Like the boss just said, all they had to do was talk to each other, find out what the job needed and do it properly. There was no need for all this hassle. He made up his mind and began to listen attentively.

Bert, sitting at his desk in the production control section, wondered whether or not it was all really possible. The boss had just said it wasn't a pipe dream, nor chasing a rainbow. He sounded as though he believed it was possible. But was it? Bert wondered. Did the boss know what life was really like outside his office? Did any of them? Were they really aware of all the problems that cropped up every day, all the ins and outs, the complexities, the forms to be filled in, the little details that had to be attended to for a job to run smoothly? Peter should know, the manufacturing director. He'd worked in production control. Bert decided to ask him the next time he came round. If Peter said it was possible then he'd believe it. Bert listened carefully, making notes on his pad so that he could ask clear questions. Maybe it was possible. Life would be great if it became a place where you could really rely on people.

In his office Neil's finger was poised over the borrowed tape machine ready to press the stop switch at his closing sentence. "Finally," he heard, "I ask you all to think carefully about what I have said. Over the coming weeks and months you will be hearing more about it, you will all be invited to become more and more involved in this process of change. The programme on which we are about to embark can succeed. But remember that we are all equally involved. It can and it will succeed only if we work together to make it succeed." Neil pressed the switch, disconnected the machine and sat back in his chair. The die was cast. He had no way of knowing what the reaction would be, how many people he had reached.

Neil was a realist. People weren't convinced by words, they were convinced by action. If he had reached the minds and hearts of ten per cent of the organization he guessed he would have done well. But it was important to know what the reaction was. He needed to know how people felt about it if only to assess the scale and speed of subsequent plans. He should have asked the question at the board meeting, he realized now. A detail he hadn't thought through. How to get feedback from everybody in the organization? A sample survey maybe? That's how the polls were assessed before a general election. Neil scrubbed the idea almost as soon as it occurred to him. The polls were sometimes wrong. No, everybody's voice should be heard. A simple questionnaire to everybody?

Neil mulled it over in his mind. It was practical; it seemed sensible. Harold could devise the questionnaire and do the analysis of the returns. Another little job for Harold. He turned it over further in his mind. The concepts and approach he had expressed over the public address seemed simple enough at face value but, Neil knew, they were far deeper than they seemed. An explanatory note was going to be issued, in fact people should be receiving it at this very moment if Simone had arranged the distribution properly. Even so, discussion was needed to make sure everybody got hold of the right end of the stick.

The explanatory note and the questionnaire would be the subject of discussions, Neil decided. People could fill in the questionnaire at the end of the discussion. Harold would do the analysis. The discussions couldn't be held during work time; they would have to be held over lunch. Departmental lunches. Sandwiches and things.

Neil liked the idea. He felt impatient, needing to know as soon as possible what the reaction was. He felt expansive, good about the whole thing. He would even pay for the lunches. Ah, no. The programme was to be self-financing; he had made that clear enough. Couldn't go back on his decision, better to start as they were to carry on. The catering bill would be paid for out of their own budgets. His managers would find the money somehow. Neil smiled. He knew about budgets. They all had enough leeway to pay for a few sandwiches.

He leaned over and pressed the intercom switch on his desk.

"Sylvia?" he said. "Get Harold up here please. I've got a little job for him."

12 *"Basic questions like, 'Do you know who your customers are?'"*

"I've got a little job for you, Dick," said Harold, standing at the open door of his office, on his way back from seeing Neil. "Shouldn't take you long but it's urgent. Got a minute? Now?"

Dick had spent the last ten minutes putting his thoughts in order before committing them to paper in a technical report to one of the project managers. At Harold's call he dropped his pen and stood up. Sometimes he thought he'd rather be a bus driver, or a plumber. It must be comforting to have a job where there was a degree of isolation, something you could just get on with and do without interruptions. He entered Harold's office.

"Sit down, Dick. What did you think to the announcement?"

"I think he got the message across okay. Took a long time to do it, though. I think he went on a bit too long, especially when he was talking about everybody having customers, relating everybody's job to customer satisfaction and measurement of how well we're satisfying them."

"Don't you agree with that?"

"Sure I agree with it. I just think he went on a bit too long, that's all. It's a simple enough idea. He'd have done better to have kept it simple."

"Maybe it's simple to you and me," said Harold wisely. "After all, we've discussed it before. Other people need a lot more explanation. It's all new to them."

"Too many words fog the issue," Dick replied. "Anyway, it's action people will be looking for now."

"That's in hand already. First thing is to get some discussions going, get people talking together about the new programme. We need a questionnaire to gauge the reaction, find out what people think about it, so's we can plan the next steps."

"That's the urgent job, is it?"

"That's it.'

Dick thought about it. "The questions should be framed so as to make people think," he said finally. "If we construct it properly it should be a good training aid in itself. Make people realize they don't know as much about their customers and suppliers as maybe they thought they did. Break a few false assumptions."

"Good. You're on the right lines."

"Start off with a couple of simple questions like, do you believe it's possible for our organization to be best in the world? Is it possible for you to be best in your own job? Then ask a few customer-related questions like do you know who they are? Do you know what is important to them? Do you give good service, is it always right, on time? Then ask the same questions about their suppliers." He laughed. "Be interesting to see the results," he said. "I doubt if people will realize the questions are so double-edged."

Harold nodded approvingly.

"You can be the very first to see the results, Dick. You'll be doing the analysis. But you've got the questionnaire to design first. It has to be out today, ready for the departmental discussions which start tomorrow. Oh, and that's another thing. Every local manager is being asked to arrange for lunch-time discussions during this week. Fix ours for Thursday, in my office. Get enough sandwiches and bread rolls for us all. Ham salad for me, wholemeal bread if you can."

Dick looked at him suspiciously.

"Who's paying?" he asked.

"I am. I'll sign an expense claim for you."

"We don't have a budget code for sandwiches, do we?"

Harold opened his desk drawer, fished out the most recent budget variance report and scrutinized it.

"Use the loose tools code," he said. "We overestimated our spending, and if we don't use it we'll be cut back next year."

Dick pushed his chair back and got up. "Who's going to type this questionnaire? I can draft it but I can't guarantee it'll be typed today. You never did sort out who's to do the regular typing for the department after Jannie quit. And she's been gone a year now."

"Give it to Sylvia."

"She won't do it."

"She will. Tell her it's for Neil. Top priority. And don't forget to arrange that departmental session for Thursday. Okay?"

Dick thought about his technical report which was already overdue. He shook his head. There was no point in mentioning it; he'd been given his priorities.

"Was there anything else, Dick?"

"No."

"Well get on with it, then."

Dick went back to his own desk with vague thoughts scratching at the back of his mind. There was something wrong about this set-up. Harold was given jobs to do by his boss and then passed them on to him to actually do. Dick had an uneasy feeling about the whole management structure. There was something wrong but he couldn't quite put his finger on it. He had his own job to do and he was getting behind in his own work through doing Harold's jobs for him. Except that Harold was his boss and was perfectly entitled to pass jobs on. That's what it was all about, wasn't it, or was it? And a questionnaire as important as this one, for discussion and completion by everybody in the organization, surely that merited more brainpower than just his, didn't it?

Normally, Dick enjoyed unanswerable questions. They allowed his mind free rein to go off on all kinds of tangents. Unanswerable questions were a luxury, normally. This one was beginning to annoy him, but it needed further thought to pin down exactly the source of his irritation. He put it aside with a mental reservation to pick it up again and think it through when he had some time to spare.

He sat down, picked up his pen and began to block out the questionnaire, scribbling down the questions at random as they occurred to him. Ranking and order would be easy to sort out on the final draft. He put his mind to work. Slowly, the questionnaire took shape. The questions Dick was asking would soon be taxing the brains of everybody in the organization as people struggled for the first time ever to find answers to queries they had never before been asked to consider, basic questions like, 'Do you know who your customers are?'

"What a daft question," Clive muttered, "Of course I know who my customers are. I've been calling on them for five years."

Clive was a field salesman, annoyed at having been called in to a special lunch-time meeting arranged by his director. The whole sales force was present, completely filling the suite which Tony had reserved at short notice in a local hotel. The hotel staff under Tony's direction had placed tables and chairs such that groups of eight were able to talk through the notes Neil had issued announcing the programme before completing the questionnaire. Clive, along with everyone else in the room, had listened to Tony's brief introduction and then to Neil's pre-recorded tape while eating from the plentiful supply of sandwiches on each table.

Clive suffered from indigestion. He wasn't feeling too good. Hurriedly, he ticked off the questionnaire. The sooner he could get out and get on with his real job the better. There was too much noise in the room with everybody trying to talk everybody else down.

There was a loud knocking as someone used a gavel, calling for attention.

"Could I have your attention, please," said Tony, in a loud voice. He knocked on the table again. Salesmen were not easily quietened. Slowly the hubbub died down.

"This question about knowing your customers. Some of you seem to be still under the misapprehension that you do know who they are. Those of you who think the answer to that question is 'yes,' would you please stand up?"

Most of Tony's staff were cute enough to remain seated, even those who, like Clive, had already ticked the 'yes' box. A good half dozen were honest enough to stand up and be counted. Tony looked across the room. His eyes settled on Clive.

"Clive," he said. "Do you really know all your customers?"

"We've only got one customer," Clive replied, "and he's the only one who really matters. The guy who buys our products. We're salesmen, Tony. All this stuff about internal customers is fine for the rest of the organization. I'm all in favour of it. Sure, we can be the best, there's nothing to stop us, given a bit of determination. It's about time everybody in this organization recognized that we only exist because of the customer. The whole programme should be geared towards him; he's our only concern. That's why I've ticked the yes box. I do know my customers, face to face. I see them often enough."

"That how the rest of you feel?" Tony asked, scanning the ones who had stood up. There were nods of agreement all round.

"How about the sales desks?" he asked. "They are your customers too. When you send in a sales report to pass on customer details, if you get it wrong they get it wrong. We end up with an unhappy customer. And you do get it wrong. Too often. Do you know the people on the sales desks? Do you ever ask them if you're giving them the right kind of information they need to process an order? Do you know the commercial people? Do you ever ask them what kind of information they need from you? How about those orders that can't possibly be processed because you've given impossible delivery promises? What kind of chaos do you think that causes for the end of the line customer? And admin, accounts. Do you know how the system works?"

Tony shook his head.

"Come on, Clive," he said, "and the rest of you. Think about it. That's all I'm asking at this stage. Our organiz- ation can be the best in the world, and it will be the best. But only when we're mature enough to admit our shortcomings. That's when we can start to learn, to build, to work together as a real team. You said it yourself, Clive. Given a bit of determination there'll be no stopping us."

Standing up had eased Clive's indigestion. He sat down and called back across the room to Tony.

"Got any blank questionnaires? Some dope has filled mine in all wrong."

There was a burst of good-natured laughter throughout the room, and a lot of hastily done corrections to the questionnaire.

"They aren't easy questions," Ralph concluded, studying the questionnaire. "How do I know whether we can be best in the world? Seems a bit far-fetched to me."

"There should be a 'don't know' box," agreed Jim. "And a 'sometimes' box for these other questions. Do you give good service, is it always right, is it always on time? Well of course it isn't. Nobody's perfect. They should have put a 'sometimes' or a 'mostly' box instead of just 'yes' or 'no'."

"There's only one answer to those questions," said Max patiently. "Nobody does everything right all the time, so just tick the 'no' box. And if you don't know the answer to the first two questions," he added, "just leave 'em blank."

Fifteen people, eleven men, four women. Packers, storemen, clerical staff and van drivers, were all sitting around the long wooden table which normally served as the packing bench but was now festooned with the remnants of paper plates, filled rolls, cream cakes, cans of coke and packets of fresh orange juice. Max had done his staff proud. It wasn't often, in fact it was the first time in living memory that he had had the opportunity to treat his department to lunch at somebody else's expense. In fact, Max reflected, thoughtfully, the only other occasions when the whole department got together as a group was when they went down to the pub for somebody's leaving party. But this was something else. This was good. Acting on Peter's instructions he had used the training budget to draw sufficient from the cash office to pay for everybody's orders. Max felt good about it, benevolent to the point of driving a van to the local bakery himself.

"I think it's a great idea," said Clint. "The whole thing. Our managing director's got real vision. It's good to hear somebody being enthusiastic about the future. Somebody who believes in us. And if he believes we can do it, so do I."

"Believing and doing are two different things," said Ralph dourly. "Things will have to change a lot if we're going to improve. I mean, look around you. Do we look like we're 'The Best'? Stock bins overflowing, no place to put anything in, we're cramped for space, no room to move hardly. And it's been getting worse this last year, not better."

"Too true," Jim agreed. "There's not a day goes by without assembly complaining about kit issues. Things are either damaged or the wrong issue, or bits missing. They're always complaining."

Max took another salad roll.

"The customer's always right, Jim," he said cheerfully. "How would you feel if you bought something in a shop, got it home and found bits missing? It's just the same."

"I'm not saying they're wrong," Jim replied, "but we can't put it right, can we? If the parts list is wrong or we haven't got the right bits it isn't our fault is it?"

Max had his mouth full. Clint answered for him.

"Seems to me that what the boss is saying is that we can put it right. Nobody else will, it's up to us. Whoever gives us the parts list, for example, is our supplier. We've got to find out who he is and talk to him, tell him where he's going wrong."

"What about the lack of space, then? There isn't room to swing a cat. What can we do about that?"

"I'll take it up with the production director," said Max, "but I don't see how he can give us any extra space, not when there isn't any to be given. It's up to us, Ralph. There must be a better way of managing the space we've got."

Ralph looked at his questionnaire again.

"Well," he admitted, "if people are going to work together to sort things out, maybe we can be best in the world." He ticked the two yes boxes and looked at Jim, grinning at him. "You as well, Jim," he said. "The pair of us, gold medallists. That'd be a turn-up for the book. Eh?"

Enid, sitting next to Max, made a scornful noise.

"If them two think they can do it," she said to Sophie

on the other side of her, "the rest of us should find it easy enough. How about it Max? Start a competition in the department. Let's have a score board. You can be judge."

"What would we count?"

"The number of complaints we get."

"Not likely," Ralph replied, indignantly. "We get a lot more complaints than you. Your job's easy. All you have to do is the counting and the clerical bit."

Max was feeling fairly full but not quite full enough. He reached out for another roll.

"We'll compromise," he said. "We'll have a scoreboard for each section and we'll count the complaints, but the game will be who is bringing their complaint level down fastest each week. Okay?"

"They'll have to be honest," Sophie said to Enid.

"I'll make sure it's honest," said Max. "You leave that to me. Now, how about these questionnaires? I've got to get them across to the quality department by two o'clock."

"I've finished mine. Do we have to sign them?"

"No. They're anonymous."

"Mine's not anonymous," said Bert. "It's got your name at the top."

"That's just so's they know which department they're from. Pass it here, Bert. And anybody else who's finished. Come on Sophie, get cracking."

"Will they tell us what the results are?" she asked. "Be interesting to know if everybody thinks the same as we do."

"We'll find out," Max promised. "I'll ask Dick."

Neil read the analysis again, for the third time, feeling the excitement rising in his bones. He really hadn't expected such a wealth of information from so simple a device as a questionnaire. Harold had done a brilliant job; he made a mental note to tell him so. The ship was launched and already they'd found a first-class navigation guidance system.

The analysis was a computer-generated histogram of total results and comparisons by division and department against a set of perceptive questions which addressed every major element of the programme. Nothing was missing.

Neil's thoughts leaped forward. This same exercise could be repeated in six months, and after that maybe on a sample basis. An excellent way of both monitoring progress and publicizing the programme again and again until it became emblazoned in people's consciousness, an integral part of the organization's culture. Deliberately, Neil put a rein on his excitement, bringing his thoughts and concentration back into real time. He studied the analysis again.

Some of the comparisons could have been predicted, like the salesmen considering themselves to be the bee's knees already. Derek's people were much more conservative. Only twenty-three per cent believed it possible for the organization to be best in the world and only seven per cent thought they personally could be best. Production people were middle of the road, except for the stores and packing department. Neil made a note to query their response with Peter. He searched on. Just as he had suspected, most people believed themselves to be better at giving than receiving. Everybody slated their suppliers and most people believed they knew their customers, except sales. Interesting. He would have to see what Tony had to say about that. And as for the majority, was it true what they believed? Did they really know their customers?

Neil resumed his study, making notes on his memo pad. At the back of his mind he could sense the ship gaining momentum and, just as vital, he was beginning to feel that the elements for controlling the organization were starting to emerge. He made another note to check with his team, to see what their reactions were. Neil leaned over and pressed the intercom switch.

"Sylvia," he said. "Arrange a board meeting for tomorrow morning, nine o'clock. Get Harold and Simone to come as well. Subject, actions resulting from the questionnaire analysis."

"It's Saturday tomorrow," Sylvia's voice replied.

"Thank you Sylvia." said Neil dryly. "I do know what day of the week it is. Nine o'clock, please. And tell them to come prepared with whatever conclusions they've drawn from the analysis. Okay?"

"I'll do it right away."

"Thank you Sylvia."

Neil released the switch and sat back, smiling. His team would come fully prepared, he was confident of that. They wouldn't want to be here all day. Not on a Saturday, that was for sure.

13 *"There's always a better way"*

Tessa was gifted with a calm temperament. Hers was a placid nature controlled by a mind that could unravel the most complex of problems, the sort of person who would have made Alexander the Great look small and inferior for having to use his sword on the Gordian's knot. She was well suited to her job, supervisor of the purchase ledger accounts, a job littered with external and internal suppliers and irate internal customers who did not take kindly to finding urgently needed goods or services held up due to non-payment of previous invoices. Money talks, often in hurtful language. Suppliers who found their invoices overdue for payment threatened to withhold further shipments until their bills were paid. It was not unknown for them to demand payment before delivery. Such was the complex world in which Tessa and her staff of nine lived and worked.

Tessa had just been to a meeting attended by all the administration department managers and supervisors. On her return she had gathered her full staff of nine around her desk and passed on to them the information she had received. There were some puzzled expressions facing her, especially Hilary, a young woman still in her teens, only seven months into the job.

"So, I'll just explain again the four things that all department managers and supervisors have been asked to do. First, get the whole department together and identify our main suppliers and customers. Second, I'm to arrange some half-hour meetings once a week with our customers and find out what is important to them and listen to what they have to say about the quality of service they're getting from us. Thirdly, I've got to arrange similar half-hour meetings with our suppliers and let them know what problems they're passing on to us. And fourthly, we're going to start monitoring, measuring if you like, how well we're doing our main job. And these measures have to be on things that are mainly within our own control."

Tessa looked at Hilary who was looking worried and confused.

"I know it sounds complicated, Hilary," said Tessa, "but it isn't really. We'll make a game out of it. You'll see."

"Harry doesn't think it's a game," said Elizabeth. "He was up here again while you were away. Shouting his mouth off because Butler's wouldn't deliver some parts he needed."

Tessa frowned.

"Shouting?"

"Well, nearly. He was very angry. He said it was the third time this week and he was going to bring it up at the next production meeting. I tried to explain that I couldn't clear Butler's last invoice for payment because the incoming goods department hadn't cleared the goods received form, but he wouldn't listen."

"Harry's job is production control," Tessa replied, sharply. "He should take his problems up with the buyers not with us. You see? That's what this new programme is all about. Putting order into our jobs. Removing the hassle. Anyway, don't worry about Harry, Elizabeth. I'll sort him out. Now these four things. I'll tell you what I think, then we'll get together again next week and you can tell me what you think about it. First, we've got three main suppliers. Purchasing who give us the order details. Incoming goods who tell us the goods have arrived and are correct. And then the supplier himself, who sends us his invoice for payment. Our two main customers are the buyers because we are completing the purchasing transaction and the accounts department for the ledger activity."

As she spoke, Tessa wrote down the department names in two columns.

"I'll give each of you a copy of these notes," she said, "so you can think about them before our next session. Now," she continued, "the second job is for me to do. I have to listen to what the purchasing and accounts departments have to say."

There was a gleam in her eye as she looked up at Elizabeth. "The purchasing meeting should be fun," she said. "Look at the number of times we can't clear an invoice because of errors on the purchase orders. Still, I'll try to be fair. We've all got to work together if we're going to get rid of the hassle. The third thing is also up to me but I'll need information from all of you so I can tell our suppliers about the problems they're giving us."

Elizabeth responded immediately.

"I'm going to start counting the number of purchase orders I get that don't match up with the invoice." she said.

"And the length of time it takes to get the goods received forms," said Hilary. "And what about those departments who buy things without a purchase order?"

"And the hassle of getting hotel bills cleared for payment," Jane added.

Tessa held up her hands. "Hold it. Hold it," she said, firmly. "We're not going to change things overnight. We'll tackle them one at a time. There's lots of problems to sort out but at the end of the day its up to us to find ways of improving our own jobs. There's always a better way of doing things and we're going to keep looking and trying until we find it. Right, Hilary?"

Hilary smiled, pleased at being singled out.

"Yes," she said, confidently.

"Work is going to be a fun place to come to in the not too distant future, said Tessa. "Not the funny farm it is at the moment. Anyway, the last thing is these measures of how well we're doing. I'm going to propose two measures that I think will tell everybody how well this department is operating. We'll keep a weekly chart showing the number of invoices which are still outstanding after thirty days, that's one. We'll also do a weekly count of the number and value of discounts lost because we couldn't clear the invoice within the discount time."

Jane's forehead creased.

"They're not measures of how well we're doing our jobs. It's not our fault when we don't qualify for the discount. If we can't clear the invoice in time it's because somebody else hasn't done their job properly, not us."

"That's true," Tessa replied. "But our main job is the purchase ledger and invoice clearance. Nobody else is going to sort out the problems Jane. It's up to us to work with our suppliers and customers to make sure that everything that goes through our department is processed smoothly and properly. Think it over and during the coming week scribble down whatever ideas occur to you and we'll talk them through at our next session."

If Neil could have listened in on the purchase ledger department he would have found full confirmation that he had made the right decision the previous Saturday. After the discussions on the questionnaire results, during which Roger and Derek had both tried to understand and explain the relatively low scores returned by their departments, Peter had made his own proposal.

"I propose that we each get our managers together to start moving on a four-point plan. Tell them each to get their own staff together, as they did for the questionnaire, and identify their main suppliers and customers. They should arrange short weekly sessions to listen to their customers and similar sessions to talk to their suppliers. And start measuring how well each department is doing its main job."

Derek, supported by Roger, resisted. They both wanted Peter to try it out first in the manufacturing division. Neil tried to reason with them, failed, and ended up making the decision for them.

"First thing Monday morning," he said, "you'll each start putting Peter's proposal into effect. This isn't something we can do piecemeal. We're all on the one ship and we're all travelling together. How can you even think of opting out, Derek? Your staff are prime suppliers to the manufacturing division. Peter can't go unless you go."

Perhaps it was the Saturday morning atmosphere or maybe it was the wearing of casual clothes that gave Derek an unaccustomed forthrightness.

"Neil," he said. "The fundamental problem is that you just don't understand the design and development process."

"There's an even more fundamental problem, Derek," Neil replied. "You don't understand people."

Roger was oblivious to the growing tension. He had come into work as requested at nine o'clock but in a bad mood, annoyed at having his weekend plans disrupted, and frustrated by his lack of success in finding a way to accommodate Neil's demand for a profit budget. He still clung to the hope that Neil could be persuaded to abandon this madness and return to tried and trusted, and above all, normal, ways of managing the business.

"You don't understand accountancy either, Neil," he said. "People who go in for accountancy are used to working with facts and figures. Their work is singular. It's not people-related."

"I can buy a computer to do that," Neil retorted. "I don't need to understand accountancy. Business finance, yes. But not accountancy. If the job is only a matter of doing sums I can replace the lot of you with a computer. I could even have it programmed to give me the profit budget you seem unable to find."

Neil shook his head. "Believe me, Roger," he said. "Your accountants are going to have to learn a whole new bag of tricks if they're to survive the coming years. And I don't just mean here, in our own organization. I mean the whole business world, wherever accountants work. Assessing risks, analysing money markets, investigating different market sectors, developing a nose for money, pointing salesmen into profitable directions, talking to people who spend money in the organization, advising managers on real budgetary control, checking our capital investments for the promised return."

Roger retreated to a defensive position.

"We do some of these already," he said.

"Well then," Neil replied. "They're all people-related. There's no point in anybody beavering away in isolation. Knowledge is useless if it isn't used in some way to improve a situation, and the only way to do that is to get involved with people, convert the knowledge into information, both ways. Talking, listening, doing. The same logic applies to your activities, Derek," he continued, tapping the table for emphasis. "Computers are doing the donkey work now, releasing people to do what they can and the computer can't do."

Neil checked his watch.

"It's just gone eleven," he said. "Unless anybody has any questions I suggest we start our weekend."

From Tessa's point of view too, Neil had made the right decision. Throughout the week following their departmental get-together Tessa had found a new spirit emerging among her group, a renewed sense of purpose almost, which evidenced itself in a brighter, friendlier atmosphere and a more positive approach to each job in hand. Within three days Hilary, the youngest and newest member of the department had come up with an idea to improve the handling of sensitive accounts. All that was needed to action it was a little help from the purchasing department.

Within the whole organization similar briefing sessions had been held and before the month was out Neil found he had another little job for Harold. He went down to Harold's office to discuss it with him.

For the space of a few seconds, Neil was in a quandary. Harold's office door was closed. Harold was inside on the telephone and he, Neil, was on the outside, holding two plastic cups which were filled to the brim with hot vending machine coffee.

"Thanks," he said as Dick came to the rescue and opened the door for him.

"You're welcome," said Dick cheerfully.

Neil hurried into the office causing Harold to look up, startled, from the telephone.

"I've got to go now," he said into the mouthpiece, "I'll call you back later."

Neil put the brimming cups onto the table so that he could blow soothing draughts of air at his burnt finger tips.

"Why do they fill them so full?" he complained.

"People were complaining that they were only getting half a cup,"replied Harold, keeping to himself the fact that he was one of the main plaintives and therefore indirectly responsible for burning Neil's fingers.

"So they have to fill them to the top? How do they expect you to carry them?"

"You have to pour some out. Down the drain."

"Doesn't that rather defeat the object? Who's 'they' anyway?"

"Maintenance. Jock."

"Give him a ring. Tell him to adjust the machines so they don't overfill the cups. It's wasteful."

Harold reached for the phone.

"Not now!" said Neil. "You can do that later."

Neil had been in a good mood when he had left his own office. Expansive enough to buy coffee for Harold on his way down. He was beginning to regret the impulse.

"I want to talk to you about all these measurements people are making," he said. "It's very good, very gratifying. I'm pleased with the way people are responding, the headway they're making, especially in the commercial offices, admin and manufacturing. Sales are doing well too, coming up with lots of new initiatives."

Enthusiasm for the subject began to warm Neil's stomach, causing his good humour to return as he expanded on examples of how people in different departments were learning from each other about the different ends of whatever process they were involved in. Making changes, improvements. He smiled, remembering.

"That Tessa," he said. "Purchase ledger. She actually banned the production controller from her department. Nicely of course, no ill feelings. She redirected him to looking into his own process instead of getting involved in hers. Actually, as Roger says, she's stopped him from causing aggravation and wasting time in her department and instead put him to doing something constructive in the purchasing and production control process."

He beamed, picked up his coffee and blew gingerly across it.

"Yes," he said, "We're going to get there. No doubt about it."

He sipped his coffee and pulled a face.

"Yuk. What's this? Turkish coffee?"

"People complained," said Harold "Said it was too weak. I'd make you some filter coffee, but Sylvia took her bag of beans back."

Neil corrected him.

"My bag of beans," he said. "Buy your own. But that's not what I came to talk to you about," he went on. "It's design and development. I'm a bit concerned about them. More than a bit concerned. They don't seem to know what to measure, having difficulty deciding how to quantify what they're doing and how well they're doing it. Surprising really. Clever people like that. See what you can do, Harold. Talk to them, get some good measures going, some improvements. If you run into any major obstacles come and talk to me about them. Okay?"

Harold nodded dumbly.

"And another thing," Neil went on. "I think we need some standard charts, so's people can publish their results. Pin 'em up in their departments, make them visible. Come up with something, will you? Make it look attractive and professional. Let me see it before you go into print."

Harold nodded, his mind preoccupied already with the two-fold problem.

Neil got up, leaving his coffee on Harold's table.

"And don't forget to phone Jock," he said. "Waste not, want not. That's something we all have to learn."

Harold waited until Neil was well clear, then picked up the phone.

"Dick," he called, "Dick. Got a minute?"

14 *"No more red-label orders, no panics. What a sweet life"*

The programme took hold and spread quickly, its roots crossing departmental barriers like the spring growth of a healthy vine. As Neil had predicted, people began to exercise their new freedoms in mature and responsible ways. Instead of having their hands tied by restrictive management practices and strictly limited departmental horizons they were now being actively encouraged to question what they were doing, the way it was being done, to investigate the finer details of the process, discard non-essentials and identify elements which were vital to the customer or the job in hand. There was no evidence of the disaster or catastrophes Derek had feared. Regardless of his warnings, people working in production were allowed the freedom to stop the process, whatever or wherever that process might be, if they were not satisfied with the quality of the outcome. No longer did they have to go and find somebody invested with authority to agree with the obvious. They made decisions themselves. And the sky didn't fall in, as Derek had feared it would.

As the programme developed it brought a fresh mood of optimism to the organization, a new vitality. People were happier, friendlier, more lively, confident. Even Roger was happy. Three weeks into the programme he had burst into Neil's office clutching a bunch of papers in his hand and without so much as a 'by your leave' to Sylvia. The only thing he didn't say was Eureka!

"I've got it, Neil."

"What? Mumps? Yellow fever?"

"The profit budget. Look."

He spread his papers out on Neil's desk, completely covering the business report Neil had been working on.

"These are the costs budgets, the variable costs budgets. Remember that word, Neil, 'variable' it's important. Now, profit. When we get down to basics, profit is the difference between income and expenditure, right?"

Neil raised his eyebrows and then nodded, not wanting to dampen Roger's glow.

"Under normal operating conditions," Roger went on, "we control expenditure on a planned basis, i.e. budgets – right? – wrong. Expenditure is planned through budgets but controlled by managers who stay within those budgets. Income, on the other hand, is planned through sales projections and controlled by salesmen achieving their sales targets. At the beginning of the period these are all hypothetical figures but the crux of the matter is that the costs budgets are looked on as real available money and managers spend it accordingly. The sales income though, is still hypothetical money and it stays hypothetical until the sales targets are achieved. So, what happens? By the end of the period the managers have spent their budgeted allowance, more or less. They've spent real money, even if the salesmen haven't achieved real sales. So, what have I done? I'm taking a provision at five per cent of the sales for that month and putting it into a special account called the profit budget, and I'm proposing to only allow the managers to spend next month what's left over after all the costs including your profit budget have been paid. See?"

Neil didn't see. Roger had lost him. He shook his head.

"No, I don't see."

"I've reversed the situation, Neil," Roger explained patiently.

"By adjusting the variable expenditure budgets every month, the managers are now the ones with the hypothetical budgets. If the sales targets aren't achieved they won't be able to spend what we haven't got."

Neil nodded slowly, knowing that it wasn't really going to be that simple.

"How are the managers going to react?" he asked. "Won't they want your blood?"

Roger shrugged.

"They can't get blood out of a stone. Besides, I've been through it with my accountants. From now on, they'll be going round the managers, advising them on what they can spend and how best to spend it. Where they'll get the best return and so on. The managers will still have the ultimate control of course but I should think they'll be wise enough to heed professional advice."

He rubbed his hands together in a washing action that made Neil think of Shylock, the money lender.

"If this works," he said, gleefully. "I'll write a paper on it for the professional society."

"No you won't," replied Neil "We're not letting every Tom, Dick and Harry in on our trade secrets. They can find their own way of being best. And what d'you mean, if it works? Aren't you sure?"

"It's new, Neil. I told you. Some of the budgets, those with a heavy bias towards people, can't be flexed up or down too quickly, and I expect there'll be planning problems, but overall, it should work. Its success will depend on how well we can guide the managers with their hypothetical budgets. Of course, if you want to back off, well . . . ."

"What's your professional advice?"

Roger didn't hesitate.

"Try it," he said.

If Roger would have shown the slightest sign of hesitation or doubt Neil knew he himself would have backed off. As it was, he gave the green light.

"Okay. Go ahead."

Roger smiled confidently. He gathered up his papers from Neil's desk and made a beeline for the door. Neil called out to him.

"Roger."

"Yes?"

"Make sure it's real money you put into the profit budget. I don't want any of that hypothetical stuff you're giving the managers. Okay?"

Surprisingly, the reaction to Roger's initiative was not as violent as Neil had feared. He hadn't taken into account the new spirit of adventure sweeping through the organization. People were expecting change. They would have been disappointed if it had not been forthcoming. And Roger did a good promotional job on his new system for budgetary control, using simple analogies, home accounts, piggy banks, paying the gas bill, the electricity, the grocer, the baker, the candlestick maker. He referred to credit cards and the horrors of being up to your eyeballs in debt, spending money you haven't got, being overdrawn at the bank. He pulled no punches. People understood what he was doing and why he was doing it and at the end of the day they cooperated with Roger's accountants. Nobody wanted to work in an organization that was forever being told how bad the situation was, how much money they'd lost, how much money they weren't making. Roger's new system was to change all that. In several departments the new system eased work loads and actually improved operating efficiency. The resources they would have used to spend money could now be re-allocated to generating money.

It was, as David commented to Robert during one of their weekly sessions, like sending your wife out to work. While she's busy earning she can't be busy spending.

"It's more like taking away the cheque book and cancelling the credit card," replied Robert.

"True," David agreed. "I've been tempted to do that more than once myself."

"Why don't you do it then?"

"Helen won't let me."

The two men smiled at each other from the shared and unassailable tower of their male dominance. It proved their resilience. Even while trying to resolve the major problem which they were now working on, they could still smile. It saved them from coming out in spots or worse.

"How on earth did we get into this situation?" asked Robert for the second time.

"A software error. Faulty programming when we put the new computer system in."

"No. You can't blame the softies. You'll have to look further back than that. Check the specification they were given. I'll bet there are lines missing in the logic. I'll bet nobody gave any thought to instructing the computer to hold memory of existing stock each time you put a modification on the shop floor. So, when you go up to issue four, for example, the data bank indicates nil stock, because we haven't made any yet, but actually there are fifty in stock at issue three, which the computer doesn't know about because they've been scrubbed from its memory by the update to issue four. The worst case happens each time you modify a top level part number. Commercial people check the computer tab, find a nil stock situation and place a red-label order on the factory for more goods to be made when actually there's plenty sitting in stores already. Production control do the same thing when they're kitting up for assembly. No wonder we've been suffering from shortages. The stupid part about it is that the shortages weren't real. We could have easily reworked the previous issues, if only we'd know they were there."

David put his head in his hands and sighed.

"What an almighty mess," he said. "A hole in the system big enough to drive a battleship through. And it goes undetected for nearly two years. That's what staggers me. How it could have been allowed to go on for so long?"

"It would still be going on," said Robert, "if it weren't for this improvement programme. Once we started measuring it became obvious that something was badly wrong somewhere. It was Peter who sniffed it out. He put the picture together and started investigating. Once you've got the lead it doesn't take long to find a hole as big as this one. Like you said, it's big enough to drive a battleship through."

"Well," said David philosophically, "At least it's found, now. And look on the bright side. Fewer kit shortages, less hassle on the shop floor. No more red-label orders, no panics. What a life, Robert. What a sweet life."

Tony didn't think it was a sweet life. For once, he was really worried, all the way back from Geneva he was worried. Six months had passed since the original BNT crisis, six relatively smooth months. Now he had another crisis on his hands.

Neil was out when Tony got in from his two-day trip to BNT. He sought out Peter as a matter of urgency, to unload his worries.

Peter came straight over to Tony's office and relaxed in one of the armchairs, legs stretched out, hands clasped behind his head. Peter hadn't felt so good in weeks, months even.

Tony came straight to the point, his face unusually solemn.

"It's bad news, Pete," he said.

"There's a real power struggle going on over there. Gomez is using his purchasing strategy to topple van Oust. Doing it very nicely too. He's developed a single source policy that makes us BNT's sole supplier for our product range, but he's worked it such that van Oust was manoeuvred into proposing us for the job. Gomez knows it will overstretch our resources and when we fall down so does van Oust."

"I suppose you didn't have any option but to accept," Peter said.

"That's right. It was all or nothing. Gomez made a play of pointing out the difficulties we'd have in resourcing the supply but he kept it very low key. It was all a sham so's he comes out clean when we fail to deliver. Then we're out, van Oust is out and Gomez is in. Top man."

Tony looked gloomily at Peter, calm and relaxed, at peace with the world, stretched out in the armchair.

"You don't look very concerned, Peter," said Tony accusingly. "Look at these contracts. How on earth are you going to supply this lot?"

Tony opened his briefcase, turned it upside down and shook it. A thick wad of signed contracts fell onto his desk.

"The volume is nearly doubled," he said. "With first deliveries starting next month. What you going to do Pete?"

Peter got up and approached Tony's desk.

"The first thing I'm going to do is, not panic," he said, picking up the contracts and scanning the order lines.

"The second thing I'm going to do is tell you what we discovered while you were living it up in Geneva. And after that, we're going out for a drink."

Tony groaned, looking up at the ceiling. "The sky falls in," he said, "and the guy wants to go out and celebrate."

Peter continued reading the contracts, one by one. "While you were away," he said, "we found a major gap in the modifications process. Remember the new computer system we installed two years ago? Designed to clean up the data base and speed the transfer of information to production and commercial? Remember? Well, what it didn't do was to hold any data on old issue stock. Each time a modification went in, the data bank automatically dropped down to zero. Nil stock. That's why your sales desks and the commercial lads have been raising so many emergency orders for the past two years. Ninety per cent of those orders could have been realized from existing stock with just a small amount of rework to bring them up to current modification state. But of course they weren't to know that. The computer tab was reading a nil stock situation, so naturally they re-ordered. Nobody thought to question it."

"Nobody?" said Tony. "That's incredible. How did you uncover that one?"

"Neil's improvement programme did it for me," Peter said modestly. "I was reading the weekly results from the measures we've been making. Kit shortages, overdue deliveries, excess spending on purchased materials, overtime in production, and so on. It just didn't make sense. I could see that we were going like the clappers but not getting anywhere. It was like we were walking backwards on a moving staircase. Then, to cap it all, Max came in. One of his quality measures is the number of items damaged in stores. Another one is the number of kit shortages he puts out to assembly. He was wanting me to expand the stores so that he could store things properly. Didn't have enough room to put everything in, he said, or to find it again when it was needed for a kit. I suggested he should set up a team to look into it, analyse what was happening and propose a way out of the problem. When they reported back it all fell into place. We've had two factories in one, for two years, Tony. Two years."

Tony was still puzzled.

"That's a heck of a long time for something as big as

that to stay hidden," he said. "Why didn't the auditors find it? When they did the annual stock check?"

"Because," said Peter, "if you remember, they didn't trust the new computer system. And we continued using the old manual system of recording stock for some time, until people got familiar with the computer version. The auditors checked against the manual records, which of course showed the true situation and so the physical counts tallied with the stock records. But the sales desks, commercial, and production control, they've all been using the data bank in the computer from day one."

A slow, wide smile began to spread across Tony's face. He picked up the contracts which Peter had put back on his desk.

"So we've no problem satisfying these orders?" he said.

"I wouldn't go that far," said Peter. "But at least we're off to a flying start. There's a varying amount of rework to be done on the older issues of course, but most of the modifications Derek has been making are quite simple. They won't cost much to action. We've got enough stock already in hand to satisfy BNT for the next few months at least. And by that time, at the rate we're making improvements, we'll be well able to satisfy these commitments you've got us into. Okay?"

Tony laughed out loud. He opened his hand, allowing Gomez's contracts to fall on the desk.

"Come on, Pete," he said. "The drinks are on me."

15 *"Best in the world applies to people, not things"*

The organization was on the up and up. It was obvious to everybody. If proof had been needed Neil's jubilant announcement which he made over the public address system, telling everybody about the major contract they had won, was evidence enough. It was possible to be the best. They had been selected from worldwide competition to be the single source of supply to the giant BNT. Of course it was possible. They were achieving it.

In the purchasing department Selwyn heard the news with profound relief. His job was safe. His future secure.

"That's a relief, anyway," he said.

"What is?"

"What the boss said, that big contract bringing a measure of security to all our jobs."

Andy was older than Selwyn. He'd been around.

"I don't want to dampen your hopes, old son," he said. "But you know the saying, 'one swallow does not a summer make.'"

"That's not just one swallow. It's a whole flight of swallows."

"Okay. But you know what happens when you put all your eggs in one basket, don't you. If BNT goes bust, we're out on a limb. And then where's your job security?"

"Give over, Andy. That's hardly likely. Not BNT. They're too big."

"Nobody's too big to go bust, Selwyn. Nobody. Even governments go bust. Whole countries go bust."

"You're just arguing for the sake of arguing."

"No I'm not. I just want to give you the benefit of my experience. You can think you're all cosy and secure in your job one minute and then, pow, through no fault of your own, you're out on your ear, walking the streets, looking for a job. Look, what happens if the competition smarten up? I mean, they're bound to be mad at losing their contracts to us, aren't they? They're not going to take it lying down. So they smarten up their operation and grab BNT off us. Where does that leave us? With nearly half our output committed to one customer?''

Andy shook his head knowingly.

''You've got to think ahead these days, Selwyn. Plan for the future. That's the name of the game.''

Selwyn dismissed him, scornfully.

''You're a right pessimist, Andy,'' he said. ''A real wet blanket.''

''No. I'm a realist. And so is the boss. He knows the score, Selwyn. That's why he's gone in for this improvement programme for everybody. You've only got to look at what we're achieving through it to see that that's where your job security lies. You know your problem? You don't get around enough. Ask Tom for permission to wander around the organization for half an hour. Do as the boss does. Go 'walk-about' and have a look at the display charts. See what's happening all over the place. That's where our security is, old son. Give us a couple of years at this rate and we'll be so far in front there'll be no catching us. Even when the competition twig what we're doing they won't be able to catch up with us. It's not like buying a new machine, or a computer system. This improvement programme involves understanding what and why, and having the courage to stick with it, like our Neil. Look, Selwyn. The advantages we gain by buying a new machine last only as long as it takes the competition to go out and buy the same machine. Machine or new computer system, it's all the same. But what we've got here can't just be bought off the shelf and installed overnight. It takes time to grow, like a tree. Provided we keep up the pace, we'll always be two years ahead.''

Andy wagged his head.

''Wisdom, Selwyn,'' he said. ''It comes with age you know.''

''Maybe so,'' agreed Selwyn. ''And maybe you're the exception that proves the rule.''

Like Andy, John, the union representative, welcomed the news. He remembered his scepticism at the inaugural meeting, when Neil had first announced the programme. John was too long in the tooth to take things at face value. A plain speaking man, of sound views based on his perception of fairness, the announcement had put him in a dilemma. He had had to choose between recommending union support or rejection of the programme. Improvement in other industries had meant lay-offs. More efficiency, fewer jobs. Neil had said that, for their organization, continuous improvement meant job security and growth.

"He's a good lad, that one," said Stan.

"Yes. We did right to support him."

"It's odd though, isn't it? I thought BNT were annoyed with us just a few months ago. Didn't they threaten to cancel their orders?"

"Yes, they did. I remember seeing the telex. I'll query it, Stan. Seems a valid question to me."

"It's good news though. Makes our jobs more secure."

"True. It just shows what can be achieved when people work together instead of just doing a job. That's what this programme is doing for us Stan, enabling us to work together. A bit of cooperation and common sense all round and it's working wonders. Who'd have believed it could be so simple?"

"It's a pity we didn't start earlier," said Stan.

"Remember that last round of redundancies? I bet they could have been avoided if we'd been into a programme like this a few years back."

Tony called his sales team together and explained the facts of life to them. He made no mention of the political background at BNT. That was strictly private information, of concern to the parties involved, and so long as the implications on his own organization were protected, Tony intended to respect their right to privacy.

"You can see the dangerous position we're in," he said, winding up his talk. "This BNT agreement is a tremendous coup for us, but it means that over one-third of our output is committed to one customer. They could break us overnight. So the onus is on the sales division. We've got to increase our customer base and subsequent sales volumes until BNT is back to a safe level of twenty per cent. This of course will put an additional strain on manufacturing but Peter assures me that he's got contingency plans to cope with the additional volume, so long as the new communication links you've established with production planning and control are maintained. That's vital. In fact, those links will be so essential, especially in the coming months, that I'm asking you to find ways to improve them even more. The ball's in our court. We've got the new targets, and a year to achieve them."

Tony grinned. "Any questions?" he asked, innocently.

The sales targets were achieved. Not exactly within the time scales which Tony had agreed with Neil, but then, they had both known, although neither one admitted to the other, that the rule they had made earlier in the year about targets, that they must be agreed, must be sensible and must be achievable, could be stretched a little for salesmen. By their nature, Tony's salesmen responded to seemingly impossible tasks. It took them eighteen months to do it, supported as they were by the whole organization. They were well on their way to being world beaters. The customer was king, whether from inside or outside the organization. The facts spoke for themselves. Even the added benefits, the additional and unlooked-for consequences of the programme, these too were major achievements in themselves, benefits like the overall reduction in hassle. Everybody's job had two sides to it. As well as being a supplier, everybody was also a customer, which meant that everybody got his or her turn at being king. It was a happy situation, reducing tension and aggravation but putting the responsibility on everyone to improve. Through a better understanding of their own weaknesses and problems they were less inclined to be continually critical of others. People rarely got annoyed any more.

Simone was annoyed, so annoyed that she almost dragged Roger into Neil's office for him to resolve their dispute.

"Roger," she said. "Being best in the world also means being the best employer. Don't you agree, Neil?"

Neil held up his hands. He knew Simone's tactics.

"That's difficult to answer," he said cautiously, "without knowing the context of the question."

"You don't need the background to answer a simple question," she replied tartly. "Since when did we put any boundaries around the aim? Best in the world means best at everything we do. True or false?"

"True."

"So along with everything else, we're aiming to be the best employer in the world. Right?"

Neil nodded.

"Within reason."

"And would you agree that being the best employer means being open and fair in relationships, being seen to be fair, providing the best working conditions and amenities? Things like that?"

"Well, yes. They seem to be good things to aim for.

It would also be good if somebody could please tell me what this is all about."

"It's the canteen," said Roger. "Simone wants it refurbished."

"And Roger won't authorize the money."

"Simone," Roger said, patiently, "I will authorize the money. We agreed at the last board meeting that the canteen should be refurbished. But not at the cost you're asking for. It's a rip-off.

"It's the best of three quotes. That's the procedure, isn't it?"

"Normally, yes. But in this case even the lowest is still far too much."

Simone breathed fire. Neil intervened.

"How much are we talking about?" he asked.

Simone laid the quotation in front of him. Neil looked at it and squirmed.

"We want it refurbished," he said, "not rebuilt. Get another quote Simone. Reduce the specification. Maybe you're asking for too much work to be done."

He looked closer at the quotation.

"Air conditioning? Fifteen thousand?"

"Have you ever worked in a hot, steamy kitchen?"

"Extraction fans I'll pay for, but not air conditioning. Change the spec Simone."

Simone didn't give in without a struggle.

"People in our organization deserve the best," she insisted. "We're all well on the way to being the best and should be treated as such. After the last financial result we can afford it, too."

Simone had played her ace. Roger trumped it.

"That doesn't mean we've got money to throw away. It has to be used responsibly, reinvestment to secure the future. We are being fair Simone, and we're being seen to be fair. Look at the last wages round, well above the cost of living increase."

"It's amenities and working environment we're talking about."

"So get a quote to upgrade the canteen into a restaurant that we can all use," Roger replied. "Managers, supervisors, operators and of course, visitors. That will save us the money and time currently being lost in taking them off-site for a meal. You can modernize the kitchen with new equipment and fans."

Simone looked at Neil who was nodding firmly in agreement with Roger. Scowling, she leaned across the desk, reaching for the quotation, a movement which brought her face within inches of Neil's.

"Make it a good restaurant," Neil added, "but in keeping with our organization. Nobody wants one that would be better suited to a five star hotel. Best in the world applies to people," he reminded her, "not things."

16 "Hold on to your vision. Stay with it"

Best in the world, an aim which had seemed to many to be an impossible dream only two years ago. Now a tantalizing destination, still far away but not beyond the horizon, not an impossible dream. Alone once more in his office Neil put aside the charts which his team had passed on to him, photocopies of the month's results from each department in the organization, even from design and development.

The programme was well established, the concepts becoming more and more an integral part of the culture. Hardly surprising, thought Neil with a wry smile. Using every means of communication at their disposal, the aim and quality definition had been tied together and passed on and were constantly being reinforced through publication of the results and achievements that people everywhere were making. The communication system itself, almost non-existent two years ago had been transformed by the introduction of briefing sessions, passing information down through the chain of command. Now, everybody was kept up-to-date with the latest organizational and local news. Everybody knew what was going on, everybody felt they belonged; they knew where they were going. They knew they were important.

Neil directed his thoughts further back in time, back to the early days, when the programme had been made an essential part of the induction training for new employees, At an even earlier stage, in the selection process, Simone had built an exploratory question into the job application form. 'This organization', it said, 'is aiming to be the best in the world. Do you believe that given the right training you could become the best in the world at the job for which you are applying?' Simone recognized that this would put an extra responsibility on her training activities but she was managing with typical female efficiency, down to the extent of providing training courses in problem solving and team working skills. Everybody had problems to overcome in their jobs. Simone taught them the techniques to show how these could be solved. And as people solved problems in and around their jobs so the quality measurements which were being made and displayed in every department, on the standardized graph sheets which Dick had devised, showed the inevitable signs of improvement.

Neil and his team had long since ceased to be surprised at the scope and range that the programme covered. It was constantly being shown to them by the number of improvement projects which were being ferreted out and tackled. But Neil knew that he would never cease being surprised, thrilled even, by the level of human ingenuity and creativity that people everywhere were bringing to their jobs. His thoughts went further back in time as he remembered threatening Harold with a change of job title to profit assurance manager. As it turned out he had got his wishes through Roger, a whole department full of them, accountants going out and advising managers on how best to control their hypothetical budgets, adjusting financial events before they happened instead of forever trying to recover from an existing situation. He recalled Roger's earlier frustration at his demand for a profit budget, a demand which was to lead him down strange and unfamiliar paths. It was the simplicity of the demand, the unarguable childish logic, the professional challenge, and Neil's own determination not to be short-changed that had kept Roger whittling away at the problem until a compromise solution emerged. The organization was now making lovely profit month by month, real money, money that was in the bank collecting interest. Neil smiled at the thought. Cat with the cream. There was job satisfaction for you.

He led his thoughts further back, to the beginning, to Dr James' surgery, where the stepping stones had first begun to shimmer with a growing brightness. The organization had been in deep trouble then, two years ago. Neil shivered at the cold wind from the past which still had power to chill his spirit. It was only now, in hindsight, that he was able to fully grasp the depth and spread of problems which had beset the organization. If the stepping stones had not appeared, if he had doubted the truth of the vision or hesitated before launching out on the journey, if . . . . Another, colder, vision appeared, of people who made up the organization, men and women he had employed, out on the streets searching for work, trying to subsist on government handouts, dependent families, bills to be paid.

Neil shook the vision away, refusing to be intimidated. That wasn't how it was. The 'what-might-have-been' had been avoided. The organization was healthier now than it

had ever been, and, more importantly, it was growing stronger
every day. All the same, he thought, strange that the stepping
stones had appeared while he had been with Dr James. Strange
too that his acceptance of the vision had been so absolute that
he had felt no need to search for alternatives. Maybe he owed
the good doctor more than he'd realized. At the least he owed
him a thank you. No time like the present. He buzzed Sylvia
on the intercom.

"Sylvia. Give the surgery a ring will you? Tell Dr
James I'm on my way for a chat. And then give Harold a ring.
Tell him I'd like to see him this afternoon."

Harold was in his office reviewing the overall results
from design and development. It had taken long enough to
define their quality measures. So many ifs and buts, so many
reasons why whatever he had suggested wasn't suitable. Long
time scales, difficulties of measurement, uncertainty in owner-
ship of the activity, no ways of influencing the results. More
time had been spent discussing the various reasons why
particular measures didn't apply than in trying to identify ones
that did. Even so, Harold had sufficient wit to realize that the
time had been well spent. Discussion of the negatives had
brought home to all the parties concerned that structural
change was needed, and the subsequent changes themselves
had contributed to the improvements that were now being
seen in the results.

Outside, at the computer, Dick was teaching Derek's
new development engineer how to do his own probability
plots. Lucky old Dick, thought Harold, in fact how lucky can
you get? Angela van Oust, daughter of the boss of the giant
BNT Corporation, came over for a three-month spell to
improve her linguistic abilities. She and Dick had got on well
together from the beginning and even now they were still
writing to one another. In fact Dick had been invited to go
over and visit the van Ousts during the summer. What did
Dick have that he, Harold, didn't? Apart from a twenty-year
advantage? Still, thought Harold, good luck to them.

He returned to the charts on his desk just as his
phone began to ring.

It was Sylvia.

"Neil's coming to see you, Harold, "she said. "At
three o'clock, okay?"

"Yes. I'll be here. Topic?"

Neil hadn't told her what it was about.

"I'm not to tell you," she replied sweetly. "It's to be
a surprise."

Harold put the phone back on its cradle and began

sorting out the charts with renewed vigour. There were surprises and surprises. He hoped this was going to be a pleasant one.

Dr James opened the envelope which Simone had given him and took out the cheque it contained. It was the latest in a series of monthly contributions from employees, the response to his earlier, impassioned appeal for money to help those in need.

A knocking at the surgery door roused him from his thoughts.

"Come in."

Neil breezed in, bright, cheerful, healthy.

"Hello Doctor. How's things?"

"Glad to see you, Neil. As a matter of fact I've been meaning to come and have a word with you for some time, to thank you for your monthly contribution, to this."

He passed the cheque over for Neil to see. Neil took it, looked at the amount and whistled.

"You're making more money than I am," he said, giving the cheque back.

"I make a point of seeing all the contributors two or three times during the year, but you I can never catch. You're a slippery fish, Neil. Too busy I suppose."

Neil laughed.

"Busy enough," he said. "Life's hard at the top."

"It's harder at the bottom." Dr James replied bluntly. "I've just read a report on where the money's being spent, the people it's helping. Do you mind if I ask Simone to put a copy in the next payslips?"

"Go ahead. I'll even find time to read it myself. I promise. Actually though, I came to see you because, in a funny sort of way I kind of identify you with the start of this improvement programme we're on."

Neil paused, shaking his head as though bemused by it all.

"You wouldn't believe the inroads we're making. Things are happening now that I wouldn't have dreamed possible two years ago."

Dr James smiled.

"I know. I do get around the place you know, talk to people, look at the charts they've got displayed, in fact I'm even using one of your charts myself, plotting the number of days lost due to sickness. And believe it or not, they're actually going down. Read into that what you like but in any case there's a sense of purpose here that was missing before you started this programme."

"That's true," Neil replied, still bemused. "But it's more than that. Much more. It's like a dam's been released."

Dr James nodded.

"I know," he said. "I've been following your programme as keenly as anybody. Listening to the announcements, reading the publications, listening to people, watching things happen. You know what you're responding to, don't you?"

"A vision," Neil replied simply. "A vision of how this organization could be, what it could become."

"Hold on to that vision," advised Dr James. "Hold on to your dream Neil," he repeated. "Keep on working towards it. If my experience is anything to go by, there will be set-backs, there always are. But don't be discouraged when you run into opposition, people don't readily fall in love with somebody else's dream, no matter how beautiful a picture it represents."

Neil smiled confidently.

"That's one of the benefits of having a one-track mind," he said. "I'm not easily discouraged. Although," he reflected, "I have been accused of having a limited vocabulary these days. Everybody thinks I've got profit on the brain. But there's nothing wrong with profit. In my book it's a good word."

Dr James agreed with him.

"In mine too," he said. "It's the opposite to waste. Profit itself is a right and good end. We just have to be a bit careful how we use it, that's all."

Neil looked at him. The doctor had this weird ability to prick his conscience without saying a word.

"That cheque," he said, indicating the envelope. "It's all from us employees, isn't it?"

"Yes."

Neil got up and made to leave.

"No reason why the organization shouldn't double the amount," he said. "Talk to Roger. Put it in terms of a charity budget. He'll know what you mean."

Three o'clock. Neil stopped by the coffee vending machine, on his way to see Harold about a new initiative from the design department. The aroma of fresh coffee smelt good, enhancing his already good mood as he waited for the young woman in front of him to put her plastic cup of hot coffee into one of the holders which Jock now provided at each location. She smiled at him and went away, leaving him to approach the machine. He felt in his trouser pockets for coins and fed them into the slot, reflecting on his conversation with Dr James, the difference in perspective between them. Set-backs, he thought. To the doctor they were obstacles. Far better to view them as opportunities for further improvement.

He smiled to himself, pressed the appropriate buttons and waited, and waited. . . .

Epilogue – use novel means to distribute the information

MEMORANDUM

From: Neil Johnson

To: Execs.
Date: January 8th

Conference—Address

At last month's board meeting I mentioned that I had been asked to present the Keynote Address at the forthcoming Conference of the Institute of Chief Executives. The topic is Total Quality and therefore, the content of my Address will be a description of how to implement a Total Quality programme in an organization.

My presentation will begin by recounting some of the successful results of our quality improvement programme and since time will be limited I would like just one example of a significant improvement from each of your areas. The remainder of the Address will concern the approach we followed to achieve these improvements. The headline notes of this part of the Address are attached and I would like your critical assessment and advice on any omissions, plus the examples, by this Friday.

On a different subject, Roger has just given me the results of the first trial-balance of the accounts and the indications are that we have again achieved our profit target for the year. Congratulations to you and your people, this was a wonderful team effort.

Neil

Attached – Draft Keynote Address for Institute of C.E.s

KEYNOTE ADDRESS

During this stage of the presentation it may be helpful to explore those characteristics which are common to any Total Quality programme. In essence I would suggest that the common characteristics are as follows:

CREATION OF A COMMON COMPANY THEME OR AIM

A CUSTOMER MENTALITY IS DEVELOPED

IMPROVEMENT BECOMES PART OF THE JOB

EACH FUNCTION RE-ASSESSES ITS PURPOSE

IMPROVEMENT BECOMES A CONTINUOUS PROCESS

COMMUNICATIONS ARE IMPROVED

BUREAUCRACY IS REDUCED

You will of course have noticed that cost reduction is not listed. Certainly cost reduction is one of the main results but it should not really be an aim. If we focus too hard on the cost-cutting side then the programme will end up being just one more of those boresome campaigns to reduce costs that come and go and really do not change anyone's long-term attitude to the job. Nor have they been successful in making us competitive with the Far East. If you have doubts on this score try writing down a list of successful companies (and successful over a longish period) who have achieved and maintained that position by being the lowest-cost producer of products and services. Of course, at the other end of the scale, companies and organizations that are not cost-effective in all that they do rarely survive and prosper. The golden rule in any cost analysis is to ask ourselves the question 'if the final customer knew how much this operation or service was costing, would he be happy to pay for it?'

Back then to the characteristics which are common to any Total Quality programme. Over the next few minutes we will look at each of these in turn, briefly explore the reasoning behind them, and suggest approaches that will assist in creating the Total Quality company.

Creation of a common company theme

At first sight the suggestion that every organization should have a recognizable theme or aim might appear rather simplistic, naive. Isn't it obvious what our aim is? Doesn't everyone know why we are here? Why do we need to state the obvious? Before we examine the need for an organizational aim, consider the aim of a nation at war. The aim is simple – to win the war. The aim is public knowledge. It is universal, owned by the population. One for all and all for one. The result, everybody pulls together, extraordinary and often superhuman effort is given to achieving that one single, simple aim. Additionally, we can all join in the celebration of successes which further that common aim. However, the provision of an aim by itself achieves nothing. As in wartime, the aim has to be supported by a well structured framework within which the aim can be seen to be achievable. But the aim itself must first be defined. Ask yourselves, around which flag are your staff rallying? Personal survival? Paying the rent? Furthering a career? Pursuing an obsessive professional interest? Lots of flags, a scattered army, all pulling in diverse directions. The result is that for many organizations the unstated aim becomes nothing more than mere survival in a tough world.

We can do better than that. We can raise our expectations, lift our horizons. We can and should supply an aim which encapsulates the culture, the spirit of the organization, an aim with which everybody in the organization can identify and make his own.

Earlier I mentioned the need for a well structured framework within which the aim can be achieved by individuals and the organization. By having a Total Quality programme effective throughout the organization you provide this common framework to which most successes can be attached. By identifying those successes with the programme you reinforce the progress that is being made and give everyone a knowledge of how much things are improving. Without this Total Quality framework the various successes of the company are lost by being distributed and not brought together under a common heading.

So, if we are all following the same guiding principles, all striving for the same aim, and all applying the same techniques, then it becomes much more difficult for cynics to opt out. They effectively become the odd ones out and are isolated when the Total Quality programme is applied, and recognized as being applied, in all departments and functions of the organization.

Develop a customer mentality

Over the years we seem to have lost sight of the singular most important fact of business life, the customer. Customers are rather important people. Remove the customer and the need for the business or service vanishes; yet every one of us can recall occasions where, as customers, we have been treated as though we were an unfortunate necessity, a distraction from what those in the organization would really like to be doing. Now at last, industry and public services have begun to realize that 'the customer' should be the focus of their attention and that to ignore this means inevitable decline in the case of private industry, and continuous pressure and public derision for those in the public sector.

So far it is all very obvious and really only so much common sense; what has provided the breakthrough in most Total Quality programmes is the extension of this 'customer mentality' into all the operations of the organization. We all have to understand that the only purpose and reason for our jobs is to provide a service or product for someone else. Everyone in the organization has 'customers' and those customers are the 'next-in-line' to themselves – the department or person they supply with the product or service they perform. Of course, the very same people who are the 'customer' of one activity are themselves the 'suppliers' to further 'customers'. And so the chain of 'supplier–customer' continues until we arrive at the final customer – the one who buys the product or uses the service and pays for the salaries of all those in the organization. This 'supplier–customer' relationship is essential to any Total Quality programme and gives the connecting path between the actual desires and wishes of our final customer and the functions and activities deep within the organization. It ensures that all of the links in the chain of supply have a direct relationship to the end of the chain and the final customer.

Making improvement part of the job

Over the last few decades we seem to have been intent on making the task of improvement a separate activity from the task of controlling the problems and activities of the day-to-day work. We have made improvement, or change, an elitist responsibility. This has all too frequently resulted in the 'improvements' being less than fully acceptable to the people who are affected by the change. At its worst, change is seen as a threat and treated accordingly. This concentration on the use of specialists seems to have blinded us to the wealth of experience garnered over the years by those actually closest to the job. Perhaps our emphasis on using specialists has occurred because we have tended to think of real 'improvements' as coming only from those large macro changes such as the introduction of a new machine, computer system, product or organizational change, which of course do need a specialist's input. But to our cost, we seem to have forgotten that improvement can also come from a whole myriad of smaller incremental improvements that, taken together, can contribute more to the effectiveness of the business than even the largest of 'macro' changes. To achieve this myriad of changes requires massive gearing and in fact the only economic route is to marshall the knowledge, skills and latent creativity of the whole organization. Our new motto then should be 'let us have a hundred small improvements as well as the big step changes'. Improvement of any process will involve the identification and solution of 'problems' and therefore, to ensure that everyone can contribute to the improvement process, we must provide training to help people understand the techniques of problem solving. Also, since many of the improvement actions will come from small teams of people working together it is helpful if some members of the company are trained in 'team leadership skills' so that they can lead improvement teams with the increased confidence that comes through training.

Promoting a re-assessment of each function

Businesses and services today have become very complex. What started out as a simple activity has become more specialized and more inward-looking. As an example consider what the response would be to the question 'what do you do?' In a small organization consisting of only a few people we might get the reply 'I work for the ABC Company'. If the same question is asked in a larger organization the most likely answer will be 'I am an accounts clerk, or typist, or ... ' – this is but one outward sign that we identify with the task or specialism, not the organization. Also in today's complex business world the degree of specialization is such that we nearly always expect promotion to be within the department or function in which we work – rarely do we see accountants becoming production managers or vice versa. With this specialization of the various functions and departments of an organization it surely comes as no surprise that, over the years, departments become self-satisfying and develop a habit of looking inwards to obtain their security and satisfaction rather than concentrating on the needs of the organization. You cannot really blame anyone for this most natural tendency – after all, who knows the real requirements of the organization? Better to stick with the things that we understand best and give the company what we, as specialists, know is best for it!

The only way out of this sub-optimization, with every department or function doing its 'own thing', is to ensure that your Total Quality programme involves each department in re-examining its purpose, activities and targets. Fortunately there are techniques for achieving this and they have a variety of titles of which the most well know are Department Purpose Analysis, Departmental Improvement Review and PAT which stands for Purpose, Activities and Targets. All the techniques have a common theme, encouraging each department, and group, to review:

- what they are doing now
- what their 'customer' departments or people require and
- what needs to be done to get closer to the 'customer requirement'.

A useful analogy for this part of Total Quality is to think of the processes within the organization as a series of chain-links, each link representing one department or activity. By carrying out improvements we strengthen each link. By re-examining the purpose of each department we make sure the links are joined up correctly with each other.

Improvement must be a continuous process

It is all too easy to start the Total Quality process with a series of projects or action teams addressing some of the company's perceived problems. These projects can be launched with grand fanfares and their successes recognized and praised at the greatest heights. Unfortunately, it is difficult to maintain the same high level of enthusiasm when you are on action team number 79! Most Total Quality programmes run into a form of crisis of diminished enthusiasm after a few years and it is essential that the programme you have been running at that stage does not just rely on these highly visible projects. To safeguard against this 'single shot' approach it is essential that improvement is made indigenous to a department's normal activity. There are several means of achieving this and it would be useful to briefly mention the main ones.

Quality Circles, consisting of a group of about six people from the same work area, are an obvious means to consider. Quality Circles have had a mixed press but the main reasons for failure can be traced to their application in isolation, rather than as part of a comprehensive Total Quality programme. Properly established Quality Circles can form a valuable part of a programme of continuous improvement. In many Companies there will be variations on Quality Circles; teams established by the manager rather than being volunteers; teams established to solve one problem and then disbanding rather than being a permanent feature. All of these varieties can be made to work given commitment.

Quality Indicators can be another powerful motivator for improvement. Find indicators of the quality of the actions or activities a department performs. These indicators should be chosen on the basis of what is important to the 'customer'. They should be displayed, for all to see, in the department performing the job. Indicators measuring 'error rate', 'lateness of delivery', etc give a visible and continuous reminder of the activities to be improved and provide a tracking of the effects of any improvement actions taken. These Quality Indicators can be very simple charts just recording the results of an operation or process. At the other end of the scale they can be quite complex charts with control limits using the whole range of Statistical Process Control techniques. SPC, like Quality Circles, requires further explanation than is appropriate here, and of course books are available on both subjects. All the charting techniques, from simple Quality Indicators to the more complex SPC, aim at increasing the awareness and knowledge of quality performance as well as providing the data to achieve continuous improvement. Properly applied, these charts become a permanent feature of the Total Quality organization.

The common features of all these approaches are that they involve practically everyone and they are owned, supported and promoted by the manager or supervisor of the department. They become part of the normal process of the department or function. It is this normalization that any Total Quality programme must achieve if it is to be successful over a long time span.

Improving communications

The establishment of 'supplier–customer' links, plus the re-assessment of functions as outlined in the earlier sections, will obviously aid communications within the organization. By applying the principles effectively the barriers between departments will be reduced and a complementary increase in knowledge on the problems facing adjacent departments will occur – this is all to the good of the organization and to the satisfaction of those who work in it.

Improving 'communication' should be a central platform of your programme and every opportunity and technique must be used to ensure that all are aware of the programme and its progress.

Together with this awareness must come the opportunity to question and contribute, and so we recommend an increase in the involvement of managers and supervisors in passing on the information by personal contacts and meetings with their staff. There are some excellent approaches that are already based on this approach and it does not take a lot of imagination to develop your own if necessary. The main points to remember are – make communication regular, use the existing management structure, and give the opportunity for discussion/feedback.

These improved communications should also be used to recognize the successes of the programme. These successes should firstly recognize the people involved in the achievement, the achievement itself should be secondary.

Total Quality involves everyone and your initial and subsequent problems in introducing and maintaining the programme will be eased considerably if you can distribute a book which usefully explores the concepts of this new way of working. You should seriously consider the advantages to be gained by giving such a book to as many members of staff as you think necessary, not forgetting that future recruits to the company will need help in understanding the background to this aspect of its culture. The concepts are much deeper than might at first appear and verbal explanations do not always achieve understanding of what it is all about. This is a new approach and every promotional programme requires more effort on communications.

Communications are, by their very nature, highly visible and therefore highly sensitive areas and one aim of any Total Quality programme should be to improve communications and to use good communications as a means of starting and maintaining knowledge of the programme, and to broadcast its progress and its successes.

Reduce the bureaucracy

Bureaucracy is a defensive mechanism to restrict variation, it lays down set procedures to ensure that the outcome is predictable. Unfortunately it also hinders change. Some bureaucracy is essential – without it anarchy results! However, an excessively bureaucratic organization delineating exactly who can do what, and specifying with no simple means of change, exactly how everything be done, has to be seen as a considerable dampener on any Total Quality programme. The restrictions that we perceive in our jobs are frequently more imaginary than real, and we should encourage the use of intelligence and initiative to generate changes in spite of the bureaucracy that is around us. Additionally, we must be prepared to reduce the real restrictions and complex procedures which limit the enthusiasm to implement improvements. Take higher risks by allowing more people to contribute to change and control the risks which are inherent in reducing bureaucracy by embarking on an education programme so that everyone knows the correct framework and company culture on which to base their decisions. Of course, even then, some less than perfect decisions may be implemented, and managers at all levels must accept this risk and not over-react when it happens; on the other side of the coin will be the vast number of successful changes implemented with no problems and contributing to making a Quality organization.

No amount of bureaucracy or procedures can cover all the eventualities of life in a modern, complex organization and so it is essential that we impart to all the staff a framework of knowledge and attitude such that, when presented with a particular situation, they know instinctively how to react and what to do. Some of the more successful retailing outlets understand this and train their staff heavily on the company culture so that, when they are presented with a problem, they can make a decision which is in keeping with the image the company wishes to present.

'Reducing the bureaucracy' completes the elements of our Total Quality programme. If we add 'The creation of a common company theme, developing a customer mentality, improvement being part of the job, functions reassessing their purpose, improvement becoming a continuous process' and all helped by 'better communications', then we have all the characteristics that make up our new way of working . . . together. Let us now review the 'Strategy' necessary for success.

Strategic planning for a Total Quality programme

Strategic planning is a prerequisite for the success of any major operation and so I will bring this Address to its conclusion by providing a final aide-memoire as a form of checklist or review to assist your planning activity. Ask yourselves, does your Total Quality programme:

- EVIDENT COMMITMENT OF MANAGEMENT? Not just by the signing of notices and letters but by obvious involvement and comprehension of the programme at the very top of the organization.
- HAVE EASILY UNDERSTOOD PRINCIPLES – The programme must be based on two or three simple principles which everyone can remember and relate to; all the subsequent developments should be fitted to the basic principles.
- APPLICABILITY TO ALL FUNCTIONS – Avoid choosing an approach which is only suitable for some areas of your organization. Go for an approach that is universally understood, and then allow a little local interpretation to suit each area.
- INVOLVE THE MAXIMUM NUMBER OF PEOPLE – Total Quality means everyone responsible and contributing; beware of programmes that allow most people to opt out by only involving a few selected teams.
- CONCENTRATE ON CONSTRUCTIVE ATTITUDES – It's far too easy for the programme to become an exercise in identifying problems for others to cure. Best that you start by ensuring that everyone puts their own house in order before 'helping' others.
- HAVE ADEQUATE RESOURCES – A large amount of training and education will be required. Ensure that you can resource this adequately. You may wish to avail yourself of the guidance and support that is now available from a variety of sources. Train internal people in the approach and techniques so that they can take over the running and maintenance of the programme.
- HAVE CONTINUITY – This is essential. Seriously look at the programme and try and imagine whether it has the potential to still be relevant in five, ten, fifteen years' time.
- HAVE A PLAN FOR IMPLEMENTATION – This should

define the various actions and time scales that will set the programme in motion and establish it as a reality throughout the organization.

Conclusion

In conclusion, one final word of advice. You may very well find that the most difficult part of the Total Quality programme is in ensuring that everyone fully understands and is fully committed to it. Referring back to my earlier comments on communications I believe that you should seriously consider the benefits to be gained within your organization by giving widespread distribution of the Total Quality concepts using stimulating, novel means as the medium or carrier. In this way you will ensure that the necessary understanding and commitment are achieved and you will have provided a firm foundation on which to build your own Total Quality programme.

Having read *Becoming the Best*, you'll probably want your staff to read it too. You may even want to incorporate the book into your staff training/induction programme. Either way, ordering bulk copies couldn't be simpler or cheaper with Gower's special discounts.

10–20 copies 10%
21–30 copies 20%
31–40 copies 30%
40+ copies 35%

Please ask for a quotation for larger quantities.

The above discounts apply to individual orders and represent a saving on the current list price.

Please see over for details of Total Quality Consultants.

The following four consultancy groups have read this book and believe they can advise and assist organizations who want to implement total quality.

David Hutchins Associates Ltd
Consultants in Quality Improvement
13/14 Hermitage Parade
ASCOT Berkshire SL5 7HE

Tel: (0990) 28712
Telex: 847738 DHAQIC G
Fax: 0990 25968

Contact: Mr F Glenister, Managing Director

DHA specialize exclusively in 'Quality' related concepts and all of their consultants have been selected for their specialist knowledge and expertise.

Since its creation in 1979 DHA have helped many hundreds of companies across a broad spectrum of industry and commerce thereby gaining a tremendous depth of experience.

David Hutchins' own experience and understanding of the need for 'Total Quality' initiatives goes back to the mid 1960s. His close relationship with the Japanese Union of Scientists and Engineers (JUSE) and such renowned men as Dr Juran and Professor Ishikawa has helped DHA to be instrumental in developing the concept of Company Wide Quality Improvement.

Mortiboys Total Business Management Ltd
Harlaxton House
Harlaxton Drive
Lenton
NOTTINGHAM NG7 1JA

Tel: (0602) 470644
Fax: 0602 484714

Contact: Mrs Janet Baines

Mortiboys TBM Ltd is run personally by Ron Mortiboys, an internationally acknowledged authority on quality and business management. He helped write the British Standard BS 5750 and the international standard ISO 9000 and is the Consultant to the Department of Trade and Industry's National Quality Campaign. The company works with manufacturing, construction and service organizations, including the public sector – helping them to identify their specific needs and expectations and make a management breakthrough based on leadership and quality – this is Total Business Management.

PA Consulting Group
TQM Division
Bowater House East
68 Knightsbridge
LONDON SW1X 7LJ

Tel: 01–589 7050
Telex: 295501
Fax: 01–225 2184

Contact: Mr David Cook

PA is the international management and technology consulting group with over 1600 professional staff of whom more than 150 have been involved in Total Quality Management.

PA's TQM Division, the foremost and largest group of its kind in Europe, is the focus for their Quality work and has carried out over 150 assignments for some 130 clients worldwide (ranging from £20 million to £10,000 million T/O) since the early 1980s.

P-E Inbucon Limited
Park House
Wick Road
EGHAM Surrey TW20 0HW

Tel: (0784) 34411
Telex: 933783 PECG G
Fax 0784 37828

Contact: Mr Len Brooks

P-E Inbucon is a leading management consultancy which conducts Total Quality programmes in 16 countries throughout Europe. With a comprehensive range of specialist services, P-E Inbucon is committed to helping its clients in industry, commerce and the public sector to satisfy the needs of their customers through efficient and effective use of their total resources.

Further information on Total Quality is available from:

The National Quality Campaign
Department of Trade and Industry
Ashdown House
123 Victoria Street
LONDON SW1E 6RB

Tel: 01–215 8142